DATA LITERACY
FUNDAMENTALS
Understanding the Power & Value of Data

BEN JONES
Founder and CEO, Data Literacy

DATA LITERACY
PRESS

ISBN: 978-1-7332634-2-9 (paperback)

Printed in the United States of America.

For Becky,
who teaches me about the good life

MORE BY BEN JONES

The Data Literacy Series

Data Literacy Fundamentals

Learning to See Data

Read, Write, Think Data

Other Books

The Introspective Entrepreneur

Avoiding Data Pitfalls

Communicating Data with Tableau

CONTENTS

This book is a companion to the *Data Literacy Fundamentals* online course which can be found at **https://dataliteracy.com/data-literacy-fundamentals/**.

PREFACE

After spending the better part of the past decade teaching people data concepts and training them how to use various data-working tools, I've learned that data can be tricky, but that we all have what it takes to become fluent in the language of data. Many people don't have that confidence within themselves yet, and my goal is to help them find it.

I've also noticed that we tend to overvalue data and we fall prey to an overexuberance about what it can do for us. Data isn't a panacea. It's inherently flawed, and only gives us part of the picture. Often it's an important part of the picture that's missing, so I don't mean to disparage data. But there are other parts of the picture, too, like emotions and instincts and even, dare I say, metaphysical elements like beliefs and dreams that are also important.

I wrote the better part of this book, and indeed I'm writing this very sentence now, during the "stay home" orders of the COVID-19 pandemic. People around the world are sheltering in place as we seek to slow the growth of a novel coronavirus. As of today, over 370,000 have died of causes related to the virus, and over 6.2 million confirmed cases have been reported. But many think that these official figures are just the tip of the iceberg. Others feel certain that they are grossly overstated.

Data about this virus has helped governments, public health organizations, and citizens like you and me track the growth of confirmed cases and deaths across the globe. But this data has in many ways failed to unite us. I am writing this in the United States, a country increasingly divided along political, economic, and racial lines.

The COVID-19 data did not cause these divisions, but we have not used the data to transcend them. There will always be dissenting views, and there will always be groups that form with similar views. That's not just acceptable, it's good. But when the dividing lines are always the same, and when the data is deputized to rationalize preconceived notions and value-based agendas, we're in trouble.

Ultimately what matters most to me is the impact of our endeavours, both *without* – that is, on our environment (people and planet) – and *within* – on ourselves as human beings (heart and mind). Data can be a step on our collective journey to a higher place, or it can be a stumbling block that hinders our progress. It all depends on how we use it.

I am dedicating this book to my wife, Becky. She helped me to do something excruciatingly difficult a year and a half ago, namely, to step away from my job and step out on my own. I wouldn't be writing this book, running my business, or doing any of this without her. Becky runs sales and business development for Data Literacy, LLC, and she makes sure we have our ducks in a row.

Becky and I are currently in our first year of marriage, a year that has seen her cancer diagnosis, surgery, and treatment; her own leap into self-employment with BeckyWithTheGoodLife.com; the loss of her grandmother and father; and a global pandemic. Through it all, she has been a warrior. I hope you have someone in your life who inspires you and believes in you. Becky is that person for me.

With that, I'd like to wish you well on your journey! My hope is that this book helps you incorporate data thinking into your vocabulary and your skill set. We're all learning to speak the language of data, and together we can help each other become more fluent as time goes along.

Ben Jones
Bellevue, Washington
June 1, 2020

INTRODUCTION

"Every moment is a fresh beginning."

—T.S. Eliot

We live in the age of data.

Organizations of every type have been amassing data since the turn of the millennium, and they have been investing in tools and technologies to help them put this data to use.

The promise of data is that we can become aware of the fundamental, underlying patterns and trends in the world around us, and that we can use this awareness to make smarter decisions to achieve our organization's goals.

This is an exciting and lofty proposition, but, in spite of our focus on data, few people within these organizations feel like they are doing it well.

And a sizable portion of those same people feel that they just aren't ready to make the most of this data revolution. For many of them, the formal education they received did not adequately prepare them for this world awash in data. Some of them are looking for a clear explanation of what data *is*, how it applies to *them*, and how it can be turned into something more valuable than just "data."

This book, the first in a series of books by Data Literacy Press, is primarily written for those of us who feel left out of this broad, sweeping data movement. Its purpose is to introduce and to welcome people into the growing dialogue around data. In order to begin participating and even contributing, we must first learn to listen – to others, to the data, and to ourselves.

If we begin by attempting to learn tools – and there are many powerful tools – we run the risk of unintentionally using them for harm. We don't ask a young person who is just learning to read to write a lengthy critical essay or to deliver an eloquent speech. They will get there, in due time.

This book is also written for those who think they *are* doing it well, but who have a nagging sense that their self-taught path has left some important basic elements out of the foundation of their data practice. For those readers, some of the concepts covered in this book will be a review. Some concepts covered will help dispel myths and common misconceptions acquired along the way. And some concepts will be brand new ideas to evaluate, challenge critically, and perhaps even adopt and embrace.

In order to make the contents of the book easier to remember, the concepts contained within it follow a simple sequence. The first chapter describes one key concept – the one overall goal of data. The second chapter can be divided into two main sections: the intuitive and the analytical thinking processes. The third chapter can be divided into three sections – the professional, public, and personal domains of application. And so on all the way up to the eighth chapter, which lists and details the eight questions to ask about our data up front.

In this way, the ideas and practices build step by step in a way that we can easily remember and adopt. For anyone who has ever tried to learn a second language, these shortcuts to memory can be very helpful on the path to fluency.

And that is the core analogy we make with this book and with the series that it commences– that learning how to use data is akin to learning a second language. In order to use data effectively, we need to be able to read and understand it, we need to be able to use it to create knowledge, and we need to be able "speak data" – to communicate it effectively to others.

In its original sense, the word "literacy" of course relates to our ability to read and write. But the same word, according to the dictionary and to popular usage, also conveys the notion of comprehension about some subject matter, such as computer literacy or financial literacy.[1]

The way we become fluent in the language of data includes some of the same approaches that we use to become fluent in the spoken and written word. We read about it and learn important building blocks. We

---

1. https://www.merriam-webster.com/dictionary/literate#h1

listen, watch, and take in the output of others. We begin formulating our own messages. We put them out there and see how others react. And we immerse ourselves in it, surrounding ourselves with those who are already fluent in the language.

This book focuses on the first of those approaches – the part where we learn the important building blocks of the language. It's only one of the approaches we need to embrace on our learning path, but it's an important one.

And it's one that many people skip, to their peril.

Let's get started!

Chapter 1

THE ONE OVERALL
GOAL OF DATA

"You can have data without information,
but you cannot have information without data."

–Daniel Keys Moran

Think about the last time you looked for quantitative information. Maybe you were interested in your bank account balance, the final score of a basketball game, or the weather forecast in a place you were packing to visit. You were either hoping to make use of the data in some way, or you were simply interested in the topic.

How did it go? Did you find what you were looking for? What did you learn about the world? Were you able to put it to good use?

Each one of us seeks out, finds, and uses data on a daily basis, like a traveler making his or her way on a roadtrip to what is often an unfamiliar destination. As we begin our journey of data literacy together, let's start by considering a very basic pair of questions:

What is "data," and why do we use it in the first place?

If we come to an agreement on the answer to these two questions, then we will have laid a foundation upon which we can continue to build.

What Is Data?

Let's start with the first part of the question: What is data?

There is more than one definition for the word "data," but in the context of this book and the course that it accompanies, as well as all subsequent Data Literacy programs, **data** is meant to indicate "factual information (such as measurements or statistics) used as a basis for reasoning, discussion, or calculation".[2]

This is the first definition given for the word "data" in the Merriam-Webster dictionary. The second definition equates data with "information in digital form that can be transmitted or processed." This definition is a narrower one, because it specifies the form that data must take – namely, a digital form. While the vast majority of encounters that we'll have with data will likely be digital in nature, we want to also include other analog or tactile forms of data collection, such as good old fashioned paper and pen.

There's a third definition for the word "data" in Merriam-Webster's, and it helps to compare our preferred definition with this alternative as well. The third definition connects "data" to the output of a "sensing device or organ." This definition is even more narrow than the second one, because it limits the meaning of the word to a subset of what we would consider data *based on how it was collected*.

There are sensing devices all around us, from the GPS receivers inside our mobile phones to motion detectors in our homes and offices to air quality or temperature sensors. And these devices, often termed the "Internet of Things," or IoT, are capturing massive amounts of data each day. But we are also interested in data that wasn't captured by such apparatuses, such as human-generated lists or comments.

Let's state our preferred definition of "data" once again:

Data is *factual information (such as measurements or statistics) used as a basis for reasoning, discussion, or calculation.*

Let's move on to the second part of the question: Why do we use data?

---

2. https://www.merriam-webster.com/dictionary/data

Why Do We Use Data?

The purpose of data is to shed light on ourselves and on our environment, to help us distinguish between truth and falsehood, and to enable us to choose sensible courses of action to take.

In a word, the chief goal of data is *wisdom*.

A well-known model exists that shows us the relationship between data and wisdom. It's called, among other names, the DIKW pyramid. This model links data (D) to wisdom (W) via two intermediary layers: information (I) and knowledge (K):

Figure 1.1. The DIKW Pyramid.[3]

It's not entirely certain who first created this model, which is often thought of as a hierarchy or a continuum, but the "IKW" part can be traced back as far as 1934. In that year, T.S. Eliot published the pageant play *The Rock*. In the opening act of the play, Eliot writes the following lines:

> *Where is the Life we have lost in living?*
> *Where is the wisdom we have lost in knowledge?*
> *Where is the knowledge we have lost in information?*[4]

It's interesting to note that Eliot not only presents the notion of a

3. https://en.wikipedia.org/wiki/DIKW_pyramid
4. https://www.google.com/books/edition/The_Rock/Qmr8AgAAQBAJ?gbpv=1

chain from information to knowledge and from knowledge to wisdom, but he seems to lament that this chain can be broken. There is a flow that should happen, but sometimes something gets lost in the translation from one step to the next. We'll revisit this idea, but for now let's consider how this early version of the model evolved.

Later versions of the DIKW model appeared throughout the twentieth century and into the twenty-first in journal articles and textbooks in the fields of knowledge management and information systems. Many of them added the fourth and lowest level of "Data," and some of them added other layers as well such as "Understanding" and even "Enlightenment."[5]

Applying this model well is of critical importance in our data-rich era, so it would be a shame if it were to live only in academic journal articles and dusty textbooks. It's a highly practical model, and one that relates to activities each one of us carries out on a daily basis, so let's see if we can bring it to life as we consider each layer one by one.

Data

We've already considered the definition of data in the previous section, so let's just summarize briefly: data is the raw material, commonly (but not exclusively) in digital form, that allows us to capture and encode facts about our world.

There's a reason that data forms the base of the pyramid. Data is a foundation for our understanding. Like the Parable of the Wise and Foolish Builders[6] in the book of Matthew in the New Testament, the quality of that foundation is of great importance. In the parable, a foolish builder built his house on the sand, and a great storm came and washed it away. A wise builder, on the other hand, built his house on a rock, and it withstood even the worst wind and rain.

The lesson of the parable relates to how we live our lives. Do we merely *hear* words of wisdom, or do we also *apply* them? And we can apply this lesson to how we work with data: do we merely *collect* facts about the world,

---

5. https://pdfs.semanticscholar.org/088d/6a1fa59a8840ab0dff0f2e06d1c1fd7d4012.pdf?_ga=2.168499109.5237240.1581957267-283478160.1581957267
6. https://en.wikipedia.org/wiki/Parable_of_the_Wise_and_the_Foolish_Builders

or do we go on to *use* them to ultimately develop a form of wisdom that helps us when the going gets tough, just like the builders in the parable?

So data forms part of the foundation upon which we build our awareness of the world around us. As we'll see in the next chapter, the full foundation doesn't only include observations, facts, and data sets; it also includes our experience, instincts, and intuition. We need to gather all of these raw materials together, we need to consider their quality, and we need to learn how to transform them into real value, as Sherlock Holmes, declares in "The Adventure of the Copper Beeches":

Data! Data! Data! I can't make bricks without clay.

EXERCISE 1.1: Write down a list of three different sources of data that you have interacted with in the past week. They can come from any area of your life – professional, public, or personal.

- _____
- _____
- _____

Information

Moving up to the second level of the pyramid, we encounter Information. What is meant by the word "information", and how is it different from data? More importantly, how do we turn data into information? Let's consider these questions briefly.

We can think of data as collections of symbols that often lack the structure and context required for us to interpret and understand them. Data points are often individual components of larger bodies, data sets, kind of like words in a book. Information, on the other hand, is data that has been organized and formatted so that it's useful to us in some way. In other words, it's the *shape* and *meaning* of the data that turns it into information.

Take, for example, the following sequence of numbers: 11032020. What does this mean? Is this a code or password? Is it just a randomly generated set of eight digits? If I tell you that it's a date, that changes the context, and gives the data a new meaning: 11/03/2020. November 3, 2020. Data becomes information.

But when data gets turned into information, a human element gets added. What is that human element? It's our assumptions about the meaning, or the conventions with which we're familiar. The translation of 11032020 to November 3, 2020 would only be done by someone who grew up in the United States, or a short list of other countries that still follow the "MDY" convention (mmddyyyy).[7] If I gave that same set of eight numbers to someone in a very long list of other countries, they would likely assume that it referred to 11 March, 2020, because they follow the "DMY" convention, in which the first two digits represent the day rather than the month (ddmmyyyy).

The map below shows which countries still officially use the MDY format, in spite of the fact that ISO-8601, which established the YYYY-MM-DD standard, was first published in 1988.

Which Countries Still Use the "MDY" Date Format?

ISO-8601 was published in 1988 with the intention to "provide an unambiguous and well-defined method of representing dates and times, so as to avoid misinterpretation". The standard ISO-8601 format of YYYY-MM-DD has been adopted by many countries, but some still use other formats, such as the "MDY" format (eg. September 17, 2018). The map below shows which countries still use MDY.

Don't Use MDY
Use MDY

Map: Ben Jones, Data Literacy • Source: Wikipedia • Created with Datawrapper

Figure 1.2. A map of usage of the MDY date and time format (e.g. August 30, 2019).

7. https://en.wikipedia.org/wiki/Date_format_by_country

According to American computer programmer and science fiction writer Daniel Keys Moran, "You can have data without information, but you cannot have information without data." That's true, if you think about it. Just because we didn't originally know the meaning of "11032020" doesn't mean that we were lacking data. It means that we were lacking information.

Let's consider the example of your bank account. Your bank faithfully records every checking account transaction, both debits and credits. That's data. But in that form, this data does not give you information about how much money you spent on food last month, for example. At least not directly.

In order to become information, we need to restructure it. But how? We need to filter the list of transactions down to just last month, figure out which of the debits from last month are food-related expenses, and then aggregate them by summing them up. In this new format, the data becomes information to us about how much money we spent on food last month. Let's say it turns out last month's family food bill was $1,285.

Here are some questions we can ask if we want to convert data into information:

- What are the **units of measurement** of the data value or values? Are the values representative of units ("eaches"), boxes of 10, or grams, dollars, or something else? If dollars, are we talking about US dollars or Canadian dollars? And so on.

- Do we need to **aggregate multiple values** into a more meaningful quantity, such as total sales over a period of time, or average height of the students?

EXERCISE 1.2: Pick one of the data sources from your list in Exercise 1.1. Write down at least one piece of information that you gleaned from this data, and how it needed to be transformed in order to get there.

- Information: _____

_____

- Transformation Steps:

  1. _____

  2. _____

  3. _____

Knowledge

The next level up as we ascend the pyramid is knowledge. As we move from information to knowledge, we add even more of the human element to the equation. Let's see how.

Many discussions and debates have taken place about the nature and meaning of knowledge, and an entire branch of philosophy called epistemology is dedicated to better understanding it. Suffice it to say that we can't solve all of those debates here, or even touch on them.

For our purposes, we'll consider knowledge to simply be "the fact or condition of knowing something with familiarity gained through experience or association."[8]

"Association" is an important word in that definition. Information gets turned into knowledge when we incorporate it into our broader understanding of the world. We do this by linking the information we take in with other information, resulting in an accumulation of learning. Those associations are ingredients that we add to the mix. In that sense, "knowledge" is a property of the humans using the information, not a property of the information itself.

American novelist and screenwriter Michael Ventura had the following to say about the difference between information and knowledge:

> *Without context, a piece of information is just a dot. It floats in your brain with a lot of other dots and doesn't mean a damn thing. Knowledge is information-in-context—connecting the dots.*[9]

8. https://www.merriam-webster.com/dictionary/knowledge
9. https://www.austinchronicle.com/columns/1997-02-28/527478/

Let's go back to our previous examples to consider the practical implications of this. If I told you that 11032020 is set to be an important date in the United States, you'd hopefully come to realize that it's likely based on the MDY convention used in that country, and you'd put a mark on November 3, 2020, on your calendar instead of March 11. But what does that date *mean*?

If you combined this information with the knowledge that the political system in the United States holds elections for federal public officials on "the first Tuesday after November 1" (or, more likely if you just searched the internet for this date), then this synthesis would lead to knowledge that the eight digits themselves didn't directly convey: Election Day!

If we consider once again the bank account example, let's recap and then carry the process forward. First, we logged on to our bank account website and thereby connected to important *data*: a historical ledger or table of debits and credits associated with our checking account. Then, we did some math and came up with the *information* we were looking for: we spent $1,285 on food last month.

But so what? How does this information help us? Well, maybe we have a reaction to seeing that number, almost like a visceral reaction, a "Yikes!" moment that says to us that this number is quite high. We associate the information with this hunch that we don't usually spend that much money on food each month. If we do some more digging and get additional information, we come to realize that this number is indeed more than we spent on food the previous month, by $310, in fact. What could be going on here?

There could be a lot of things, but the bottom line is that we have converted data to information, and information to knowledge. We have some more information to gather, and more thinking to do to complete the process, but for now we have succeeded in using data at our disposal to acquire knowledge about our corner of the world.

Here are some questions we can ask if we want to convert information into knowledge:

- What is the context of the data?
- When was the data collected, by whom, and for what purpose?
- With what is the data associated?

- What comparisons can we make to help us better grasp the relevance of the data?

EXERCISE 1.3: Take the information from Exercise 1.2 that you extracted from your chosen data source, and ask yourself what knowledge you have gleaned from that. List any associations with other information or experiences that you needed to make in order to turn that information into knowledge.

- Knowledge Gleaned: _____

- Helpful Associations:

  1. _____

  2. _____

  3. _____

Wisdom

And finally we reach the pinnacle of the pyramid, wisdom. Wisdom is also a concept with many and varied definitions. What does it mean in this context, and how does it relate to data and data literacy? Let's explore the idea.

We start with data *collection*, and then in order to turn that data into information we need to carry out accurate *interpretation*. And if we get from information to knowledge by making *associations*, then we get from knowledge to wisdom by correct *application*:

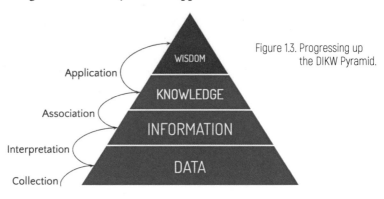

Figure 1.3. Progressing up the DIKW Pyramid.

Motivational author Dr. Roopleen stated the following about the difference between knowledge and wisdom:

Learning is a matter of gathering knowledge;
wisdom is applying that knowledge.

Wisdom alone among the four levels of the pyramid involves the ability to choose the right course of action. And once again, the trend holds that the higher up the pyramid we go, the more we as humans add to the equation. Wisdom involves beliefs, values, and principles of ethics, all intensely human elements.

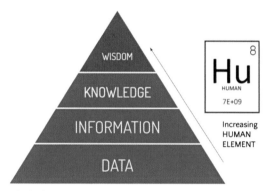

Figure 1.4. The higher up pyramid we go, the more we add the "human element."

As Eliot warned us in his play, just because we have plenty of knowledge, that does not mean we have found our way up to wisdom, the highest level of the pyramid. His warning has proven accurate in our era, often thought of as the "Data Revolution." Organizations in recent times have used data in unethical ways to extract an unfair profit. From social media platforms that sell customers' private data without their consent to organizations that take inadequate measures to safeguard sensitive data, to algorithms that propagate biases. It would be better for a team not to be data literate at all than for them to use data for harm.

Let's go back to our two examples in order to illustrate the transformation of knowledge into wisdom. Perhaps we're planning a large corporate conference. We had been given a really low quote from a convention center for this very week, and we were ready to sign the contract to schedule our 14,000-person event.

Now, armed with the knowledge that November 3, 2020 is the date of the federal elections in the United States, we realize it would be unwise to do so, and could lead to both low attendance as well as unhappy attendees. We started with the data point "11032020" and we ended up with a date on the calendar to avoid at all costs. Phew!

With the example of the bank account and the month with the abnormally high food expenditures, we might gather additional information and realize that we hadn't ever spent more than $1,000 on food during any month within the past year. We feel even more confident that the $1,285 month was an anomaly. We had neglected our habit of bringing in dinner leftovers for lunch and instead opted to eat out with groups of coworkers most days during the month. An analysis of the food category expenditures reveals 28 restaurant trips instead of the 11 from the previous month. It might be a wise course of action to go back to bringing in leftovers in order to save the budget next month.

We may have blown the budget, but did we make up for it in career growth potential? We definitely got to know some of our coworkers better over the course of the month, and even a couple of the executive leaders of the company. Maybe spending on food in this way is better for our family finances after all. But how about our health? Had we put on weight over the course of the month? Could this lead to a life with a higher-paying job as well as higher healthcare bills?

As we see with this example, applying wisdom doesn't necessarily mean that we just let a single piece of knowledge dictate our actions. It doesn't usually work that way, because our most important decisions typically involve multiple factors. Some of these factors have trustworthy data and some do not. There is also uncertainty in the future and whether current trends will carry forward or not. This is why we should seek to make *data-informed* decisions rather than *data-driven* decisions. Data shouldn't drive our decisions. We should be in the driver's seat. Data is an incredibly useful resource for us, especially when we turn it into information, and then knowledge, and then wisdom.

In the Data Literacy: Level 2 course, we will consider the transformation from data to wisdom in even more detail, laying out a framework and a flowchart to follow as you learn how to put data to good use in your own situation.

EXERCISE 1.4: Returning to the example you've been developing in the previous exercises in this chapter, see if you can think of an unwise course of action and a wise course of action that would stem from application of the knowledge you have gleaned thus far.

- A wise course of action to take: _____

  _____

  _____

- An unwise course of action to avoid: _____

  _____

  _____

Chapter 2

THE TWO SYSTEMS
OF THINKING

"Intuition will tell the thinking mind where to look next."

—Jonas Salk

I n 2014, a large technology company ran a television advertisement pro-
moting their business intelligence platform. The advertisement showed
a number of their customers being interviewed on camera in very short
segments, and one of the people had the following to say:

We used to use intuition; now we use analytics.

This quote seems to indicate that intuition and analytics are mutually
exclusive approaches to working and making decisions. The implication is
that using analytics is much better than using intuition. In the bestselling
2008 book *Super Crunchers*, author Ian Ayres states, "We are in a historic
moment of horse-versus-locomotive competition, where intuitive and expe-
riential expertise is losing out time and time again to number crunching."
He goes on to issue the ominous warning "Intuitivists beware." Chilling.

You may not have read this book or seen the commercial referred
to above, but you've probably noticed the hype around data that seems
to tell us that data is here to save us from our flawed and dangerous
instincts. This is a misconception.

Data and analytics are useful and their increasing usage amounts to another industrial revolution, without a doubt. They shouldn't, however, be thought of as a *replacement* for other modes of human thinking, but rather as a powerful *complement*.

That's not a typo, by the way, and we don't mean to say that they amount to a *compliment*: "a polite expression". We mean that they're a *complement*: "something that fills up, completes, or makes better or perfect".[10]

In this chapter, we'll explore this idea, which is central to developing data literacy.

In order for us to understand the power and value of data, we first need to understand some basic principles about how our mind works. So let's think about our thinking! First, though, a few short exercises to get the blood flowing.

EXERCISE 2.1: Take a look at the photograph below. What one word would you use to describe how you think this child feels?

A: _____

Figure. 2.1. The joy of the happy face by Rasheedhrasheed.[11]

---

10. https://www.merriam-webster.com/dictionary/complement
11. https://commons.wikimedia.org/wiki/File:The_joy_of_the_happy_face_by_Rasheedhrasheed.jpg

Did you need to stop and think about it for a while, or did the answer come automatically to your mind without any mental effort? Most likely you'll answer the latter. Recognizing emotions from facial features is a highly intuitive task. As humans, we don't stop and analyze the angle of the contours of the person's mouth or eyes, and no spreadsheets or databases are involved.

We just see the photograph, and the thought immediately springs to our mind: this child is happy! It's almost impossible to stop this thought from happening. It makes sense, then, that the word "intuition" comes from the Latin word *intuērī,* which means "to look at, to gaze upon."

EXERCISE 2.2: Now, let's try another thought experiment. How many different triangles can you find in the image below (not including the one in the "A" of the caption):

A: _____

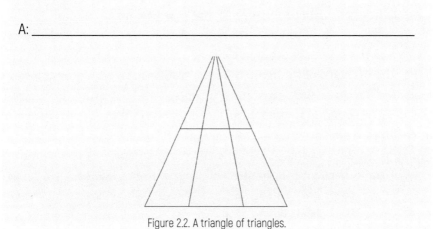

Figure 2.2. A triangle of triangles.

The answer is at the end of the chapter, so you're on the honor system to come up with your own guess before checking. At the moment, however, let's consider your thought process with this second exercise. It involved a lot more effort than the first exercise, didn't it? Unless your mind works very differently than most other human minds, the answer didn't surface automatically and effortlessly like it did with the question about the child's emotions in the photograph. You had to think about it. This process was slow and deliberate. You had to reason your way through the puzzle.

These two exercises involved two very different types of thought processes.

Two Systems of Thinking

In the past half century, researchers have developed an amazing amount of knowledge about the way our brains work. This research has often come from controlled behavioral experiments, some of which include new means of detecting activity in the brain, such as the fMRI, or functional magnetic resonance imaging. This technique, which has been used since the early 1990s, detects changes associated with blood flow to different areas of the brain when various types of mental tasks are being carried out by the subject of the experiment.

Cognitive psychologists, behavioral economists, and philosophers have come to describe the way the brain works using a helpful metaphor: System 1 and System 2 thinking. According to this model, there are two distinct types of thought that each one of us carries out on a daily basis. The first type of thought, System 1 thinking, is fast, automatic, and reflexive. We often use words like "intuitive" and "creative" to describe the kinds of thinking for which System 1 is responsible. The first exercise of looking at the photograph of the child's face involved this kind of thinking. So does adding 2 + 2. The answer just pops into your mind.

On the other hand, System 2 thinking is slow, effortful, and reflective. We use words like "analytical" and "logical" when we refer to System 2 processes. This is the type of thinking that kicked into gear when you studied the lines in the image and tried to find and count the different triangles it contains. Or when you try to multiply 16 x 33.

This notion that there are two distinct ways of thinking is called "dual process theory." Nobel prize winner Daniel Kahneman relayed this concept to a modern lay audience in the book *Thinking, Fast and Slow*[12] in which he describes various learnings that he gleaned from experiments he often ran in collaboration with fellow Israeli psychologist Amos Tversky.

12. https://en.wikipedia.org/wiki/Thinking,_Fast_and_Slow

In the first chapter of the book, Kahneman is careful to point out that while he speaks of these two systems as if they are two separate characters in our mind, this is really just a useful shorthand that saves us from having to use their distinct characteristics every time we refer to them. There aren't really two different characters in our minds, and these thought processes don't entirely emanate from separate areas of the brain, like the popular "right brain" versus "left brain" concept would have us believe. It's a lot more complex than that, and we're only just starting to map it out.

So how does all of this relate to working with data, and becoming highly data literate? Well, when we make sense of the world using data, we typically think of ourselves as conducting deliberate analysis, and carrying out conscious reasoning. These are System 2 activities.

And while this is true, it's only partly true. It turns out that our intuitive thought processes can still be active and engaged while we are analyzing. Rather than seeing these two modes of thought as a horse-versus-locomotive competition, we can instead see them as two elements of the same engine that can work in tandem with one another.

In fact, this is what researchers have come to understand about System 1 and System 2: that they are "two parallel interactive modes of information processing, served by separate cognitive systems."[13] In other words, having more of one doesn't necessarily mean we have to have less of the other.

This is great news for people who are new to working with data! You don't need to check your experience and intuition at the door. In fact, you can put those very assets to good use when you work with data. Let's explore how.

The Five Roles of Intuition in Analytics

Simply put, if "data is the new oil," then human intuition is the spark that ignites the analytics engine. Let's consider five different ways in which we can use intuition and analysis together to make better decisions than if we just used one or the other.

---

13. Intuition: A fundamental bridging construct in the behavioural sciences, Hodgkinson, Langan-Fox, Sadler-Smith (2008).

1. Knowing what the data is telling us and not telling us

When we analyze data, there's a sense in which our intuition is helping us to determine what the data is telling us, and what it's not telling us. Alberto Cairo, Knight Chair at the University of Miami and author of *How Charts Lie* and *The Functional Art*, provided this quote for the ebook *17 Key Traits of Data Literacy* (emphasis mine):

> *Working with data requires a certain degree of numerical and graphical literacy, respectively called numeracy and graphicacy. Numeracy isn't just the mathematics, statistics, or logic, but **a sixth sense** that is grounded on a grasp—even a tenuous one—of fundamental concepts of those areas. Graphicacy, on the other hand, consists of developing **intuitions** of what kinds of graphs, charts or maps are more adequate to either explore our data or communicate the main insights we obtained to other people.*

Did you notice Cairo's emphasis on the human element of working with data? Data may be concrete, but our interaction with it can be fuzzy. We need to develop an intuition about how to work with the data, similar to the way we needed to learn how to walk or ride a bike. That kind of know-how comes with experience and the trial and error that comes along with it.

2. Knowing where to look next

As we'll discuss in Data Literacy Level 2, exploratory data analysis (often termed EDA) is a highly iterative process. We might start down one line of inquiry with a data set only to be pulled into a completely different direction. Often this change in course is triggered by nothing more than a hunch.

Other times we get to the end of a particular analysis and, while we may have received the answer to our original question, the data actually points us to a different, much more interesting question altogether. Perhaps we notice a quirky pattern in the data, or we can't help but spot a conspicuous outlier. We have this funny feeling that we've stumbled on a trail we need to follow.

Jonas Salk, the American medical researcher and virologist commonly credited with discovering the polio vaccine, had the following to say about intuition that captures this point perfectly:

Intuition will tell the thinking mind where to look next.

3. Knowing when to stop looking and take action

There is a well-known term, "analysis paralysis", that describes the condition in which we can't come to a decision or move forward because we're stuck in the data. There's no end to the different avenues of analysis that we can potentially go down, and it's possible to apply System 2 thinking for far too long. Each decision has a finite window of time in which we need to act, and the adept analyst knows when it's time to stop crunching numbers and make a move.

The game of chess provides us with a fitting example. In a timed chess match, there are two adjacent clocks, one for each player, that count down a set time allotted for each player to move their pieces. When one player moves their piece and hits a button on their side, their clock stops counting down and the other player's clock starts up again.

Figure 2.3. BlindenSchachuhr.jpg by Mussklprozz.

Players can win by placing their opponent into checkmate, or by having time remaining on their clock when the other player's clock hits zero. Therefore, skilled chess players must balance the need for thorough assessment of each move along with the need to move quickly enough so that they leave themselves enough time for future moves.

It's fitting, then, that Russian chess Grandmaster Garry Kasparov had the following to say in his book *How Life Imitates Chess* about where this sense of balance comes from:

> *Something has to tell you when the law of diminishing returns is kicking in. And that something is intuition.*[14]

Of course, the difference between life and chess is that in most situations, we don't know exactly how much time we have to make a decision. If we wait until next week to make an offer on a house, will the seller be more willing to accept a lower offer, or will it no longer be on the market? If we decide to wait a few extra months to add a couple more features to a product we're developing before launching it, will those features save the product from failure, or will our competitors launch in that time and claim the first mover advantage?

We can gather data to inform us how to make wise decisions as well as when to make them, but there's almost always a degree of human intuition in the equation that helps us make the final call.

4. Knowing who needs to hear and how to get through to them

After we've found an important insight in data, we'll likely need to relay that information along with the knowledge we glean from it to other people. Communicating with other people is an intensely human activity that involves visual, verbal, and nonverbal cues passed back and forth between us.

Before we even start communicating, though, we need to figure out who needs to know. How many times have we reached the end of a fabulously delivered presentation only to find out that the wrong people were

14. https://www.amazon.com/How-Life-Imitates-Chess-Boardroom/dp/1596913886

in the room? Intuition about the people and organizations with which we interact helps us know who the decision makers are, and how we can get on their calendar.

Once we identify the right people we need to know how to get through to them. What messages will have the intended impact, what messages will fall flat, and which will backfire? In order to answer these questions, we need to develop a keen intuition about the art of persuasion. This is another way in which our analytical abilities coupled with our intuition can make a difference.

There's an interesting quote by Russell Conwell, founder of Temple University, that illustrates this concept. He gave a famous presentation titled "Acres of Diamonds" more than 6,000 times. He had this to say about his approach:[15]

> *I visit a city or town, and try to arrive there early enough to see the post-master, the barber, the hotel manager, the principal of the schools, some of the ministers, and then go into the stores and talk with the people, and see what has been their history and what opportunities they had. Then I give my lecture and talk to those people about the subjects that apply to them locally.*

In this way, Conwell was not only able to gather information about his audience, but he was able to use his senses to learn about them as individuals: their concerns, their style, their mannerisms. He may have had an important message to deliver to them, but unless he developed an intuition about how to get through to them, his presentation would have fallen on deaf ears.

5. Knowing why any of it matters in the first place

There are an infinite number of matters with which we can concern ourselves. Which ones are important and which ones are irrelevant? The common quip about "rearranging deckchairs on the Titanic" brings home

---

15. https://www.amazon.com/Quick-Easy-Way-Effective-Speaking/dp/0671724002

the point. It's possible to spend our time with activities that don't matter, while simultaneously neglecting other potentially life-saving matters.

And once we focus on what we think are critical matters, how do we measure things related to those matters? What data do we collect to help us chart our path? There are a dizzyingly large number of metrics we can collect about even the simplest of topics. What are the "Key Performance Indicators" (KPIs) for our situation? This is where experience and intuition about the subject matter at hand can make an enormous difference, and why we look to hire and partner with people who have been there and done that.

You're running a start-up technology company and you're in the second year of operation. When you consider your financial performance, do you focus on revenue, profitability, cash flow, "burn rate," or something else? Is there a point in time in which your primary focus shifts from one metric to another? What is the reason for that shift?

Data and analytics can be powerful, but unless we have a keen intuition about our environment and what really matters, we run the risk of developing incredible amounts of knowledge about topics that don't matter at all. The following Albert Einstein quote applies:

The only real valuable thing is intuition.

The Dark Side of Intuition

We've considered ways in which intuition can be incredibly valuable, and should not be written off or discounted in the data-informed decision-making process. For this reason, a healthy appreciation for intuition and experience is appropriate. But just like data and analytics, intuition and experience are quite fallible. How so?

Well, just because we have a strong intuition about something doesn't mean that we're right. We sometimes recoil from objects that turn out to be garden hoses rather than snakes. Consider the following pair of lines, for example. If you look only at the straight portion between the arrowheads, what does your gut tell you about which is longer, the one on the top or the one on the bottom?

Which line is longer?

Figure 24. Visually comparing the lengths of two lines.

Of course, these two line segments are exactly the same length. The arrowheads create an optical illusion that tricks our brains into thinking the one on the bottom is longer, but it isn't. That same visual system that gave us such an accurate visceral answer about the emotion of the child at the beginning of the chapter failed us miserably in this task.

And it isn't just visual tasks that can trigger wrong intuitive responses that feel very right. Consider the classic question posed by researchers about the cost of two items:[16]

- A bat and a ball together cost $1.10.
- The bat costs $1.00 more than the ball.
- How much does the ball cost?

Many respondents to this straightforward but tricky quiz feel an initial urge to answer that the ball costs $0.10, but this answer is incorrect. If that were the case, the bat would cost $1.10 by itself (since it costs $1.00 more than the ball, or Bat = $1.00 + Ball), and the two together would cost $1.10 + $0.10 = $1.20.

The correct answer is that the ball costs $0.05 and the bat costs $1.05, which satisfies both conditions, but this isn't typically our first thought. It's an elementary algebraic problem with two equations and two unknowns, but our intuitive mind wants to jump to a convenient answer that feels right. Such an intuitive shortcut would once again lead us astray.

16. https://pdfs.semanticscholar.org/4069/615a36c33e61ca309b8ceaeb628a10d441b5.pdf

As researchers have learned about the way the human brain works, they have discovered that we use a plethora of "heuristics," or shortcuts to cognition to deal with a complex environment.

These shortcuts are incredibly useful, but they leave us susceptible to fairly egregious biases. For example, the confirmation bias leads us to tend to accept information that backs up our previously held beliefs, and reject or completely tune out information that challenges those same beliefs. The availability heuristic makes us think that something that readily comes to mind is more common than it is, such as deaths by terrorism (which is incredibly rare) compared to deaths by heart disease (which is a epidemic in civilized countries).

Sometimes, our analysis backs up our intuitions, and everything is hunky dory. Other times these two systems of thought are at odds with one another. Our intuition might be telling us that our data or analysis are flawed in some way. Alternatively, our analysis might be uncovering a bias in our way of thinking. How are we to know which system is to be trusted? We need to look further at the matter. Turning off one system or the other might make the decision-making process simpler for us, but we'll likely make more mistakes.

Earlier in this chapter we mentioned Daniel Kahneman and his book *Thinking, Fast and Slow.* In an address at the World Business Forum in New York, Kahneman gave the following three questions to ask yourself in order to know whether it's reasonable to trust your gut:[17]

1. Is there some degree of regularity in a particular area that you can pick up and learn?

2. Do you have a lot of experience in this area, and have you practiced in it for some time?

3. Have you received immediate and concrete feedback in the past to help inform your gut?

---

17. https://www.thinkadvisor.com/2018/11/16/daniel-kahneman-do-not-trust-your-intuition-even-f/

An Idea Rooted in Antiquity

The notion of there being two distinct but interrelated types of thinking—intuition and analysis—is rooted in antiquity. Around 370 BCE, Plato, in his discourse *Phaedrus,* compared the human soul to a charioteer driving a chariot pulled by two horses: a well-behaved white horse and a troublesome black horse.[18]

Figure 2.5. "Driving a Chariot Using a Snake Whip" by Alex Proimos, shared under CC 2.0.

In Plato's analogy, the charioteer represented the human intellect, or reason, and the two horses represented human passion in the form of both moral and immoral emotions. System 1 thinking, or intuitive thought, is often linked with the emotions, and System 2 thinking is often linked with reason.

A very similar analogy can be found in the Katha Upanishad, part of the Vedas, an ancient Sanskrit text that forms the spiritual teaching and ideas of Hinduism potentially dating as far back as 800 BCE.

18. Plato, *Phaedrus* (New York: Penguin Books, 2005), p. 36.

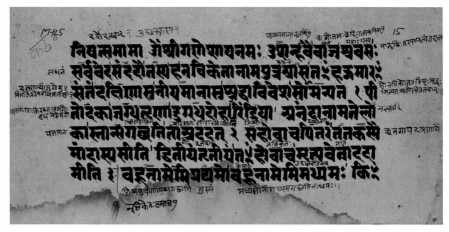

Figure 2.6. "Katha Upanishad 1.1.1 to 1.1.3 verses, Krishna Yajurveda," by Ms Sarah Welch.

This passage reads as follows:

> *Know the Self as lord of the chariot,*
> *The body as the chariot itself,*
> *The discriminating intellect as*
> *The charioteer, and the mind as reins.*
> *The senses, say the wise, are the horses.*

So it seems that this notion of the different parts of the human mind and soul dates back quite a long way. It's fascinating that these ancient texts speak of the combination of these elements, and of the ability of the intellect to harness the intuitions and emotions, and to put them to work rather than being dominated by them.

If you're new to data, please be disabused of the false notion that data will save you from your flawed intuition. Perhaps we can rewrite the statement in the television advertisement at the beginning of the chapter in such a way that we will incorporate both of the two systems of thinking, instead of just one or the other:

> *We used to use intuition. Then we used analytics. Now we use both.*

Oh, and back to our triangle puzzle: there were 12 triangles to be found in the image:

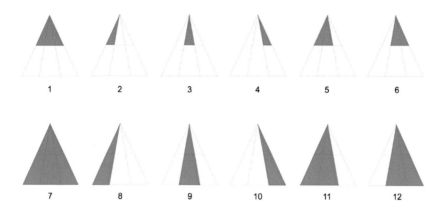

Chapter 3

THE THREE DOMAINS
OF APPLICATION

"Never get so busy making a living that you forget to make a life."
–Dolly Parton

In what areas of life do we use data? In this chapter we'll consider different domains of application for data, and we'll expand our notion of the value of data beyond the workplace. Let's dive right in with a free response exercise.

EXERCISE 3.1: Why do you want to become more fluent in the language of data? Come up with three different reasons why you are looking to improve your data knowledge and skills:

1. _____

2. _____

3. _____

Now go back and look at your list. How many of your top reasons relate to your professional life or employer? Likely most of them, if not all.

It makes sense that we would consider data skills in the context of our careers. When we hear about data, it's often about job skills that are in demand, or companies that are pushing the boundaries of technology, or it's part of a job title like "data analyst" or "data scientist." We typically think of data skills in the context of professional pursuits.

But there's no need to confine data to the four walls of our employers. Data is as relevant to societies seeking to create a peaceful and functional world as it is to companies seeking to grow profits. It's also just as relevant to our own personal lives as we seek to develop into our best selves. Let's consider each of these three domains that together form the three Ps: professional, public, and personal. In doing so, we will broaden our perspective about what fluency in data can help us accomplish both independently and together.

Professional Domain

The dominant economic system in the twenty-first century world is capitalism. Goods and services are exchanged in markets in which companies, both privately and publicly held, compete for customers and market share. Wealth is invested by individuals and organizations in financial and capital markets seeking to increase their net worth. Governments around the world exercise varying amounts of influence and control within this system, either by regulation or by state ownership of assets or other means. But for the most part, non-government corporations own the means of production and profit.

The past two and half centuries have produced three major industrial revolutions in the world, and many believe we are in the beginning stages of a fourth. The First Industrial Revolution that started in the mid-eighteenth century involved a shift from hand-production to mechanized factories powered by steam, water, and coal. Then, about a century later, the Second Industrial Revolution kicked off as electricity enabled manufacturing to shift to mass production. The telephone and the automobile emerged from this revolution, and the world became more connected.

Fast forward another century to the mid-twentieth century and we arrive at the Third Industrial Revolution, also called the Digital

Revolution. The invention and proliferation of computers and digital record keeping in the past half century has led to the Information Age in which we find ourselves today. This massive leap forward in technological capabilities has had major ramifications on how we spend our time while at work. That applies to people who work in the private sector, but also for those who work in the public sector (government agencies) and the voluntary sector (nonprofit organizations).

The pace of innovation in the past four decades has accelerated dramatically, and we have had to learn new skills to keep up with the times. In the 1980s, as computing moved from mainframes to the desktop, professionals in all sectors and industries had to learn basic computer skills such as word processing in order to contribute in the workplace. Then, in the 1990s, with the advent of the internet, navigating the World Wide Web became a requirement for virtually every white-collar job. After the turn of the millennium, the social media wave hit, and professions focusing on data (data entry, data engineering, database management, data analytics) started rapidly expanding as well.

And since 2010, with the rapid expansion of the self-service analytics movement, the need to read, interpret, create, and communicate with data has risen by leaps and bounds. It's no longer just data specialists who need to make sense of data; everyone does. And for many of us living and working at the cusp of this next revolution, our formal education did not prepare us for this new reality. We are having to acquire new data knowledge and skills while on the job.

Consider the skills that companies need the most in 2019.[19] Out of 50,000 different skills, the top 25 "hard skills" includes many that are anchored in the data realm such as artificial intelligence, analytical reasoning, natural language processing, scientific computing, business analysis, and data science.

And we can take a look at how worldwide relative search interest on Google for a number of popular data job titles has changed over the past decade:

---

19. https://learning.linkedin.com/blog/top-skills/the-skills-companies-need-most-in-2019--and-how-to-learn-them

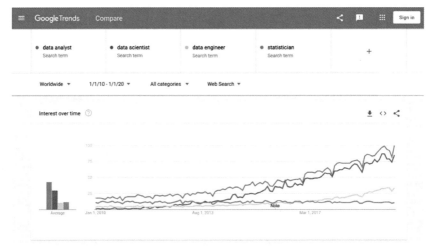

Figure 3.1. A decade of change in worldwide relative search interest in data job titles.

Notice that "data analyst", "data scientist" and "data engineer" have all increased in worldwide search interest over this time, but interest in "statistician" has not. This is partly explained by the fact that those with an education in statistics are now applying for and landing jobs with titles such as "data scientist" and the like. But it's clear that the overall search interest for the new terms has grown well beyond where it was only a decade ago.

Whether we're talking about skills or job titles, there's no doubt that data has become a critical, enabling raw material for the Fourth Industrial Revolution that is taking shape and affecting companies in every single industry. This is one major reason that data literacy is so critical for each of us to develop. As we'll see in the next section, though, it's not the only reason.

EXERCISE 3.2: Let's consider your current job. Which of the following forms of data have you used in the past month at work?

☐ A single chart or graph
☐ A spreadsheet or a data file
☐ A cloud-based data source

☐ A dashboard (more than one chart in a single view)
☐ A report or presentation including data

Public Domain

If we stopped there and only used data to achieve professional goals relative to commerce and profit, then data would fall far short of achieving it's true potential for our world and our species. Worse than that, actually—it's possible that it would do more harm than good.

That's because one of the chief criticisms of capitalism is that it prioritizes corporate profitability over the health of our societies and our environment. What's to stop a factory from taking advantage of an impoverished workforce in order to drive down production costs? Who will stand in the way of an industrial chemical company dumping waste into a river to avoid incurring costs associated with proper disposal?

Government regulation theoretically acts as a counterbalancing force against the worst such corporate abuses, and it can be effective to a degree. But what happens when the politicians' pockets are lined with donations from the very people who are guilty of these offenses? Or when their reelection campaign depends on favorable economic indicators in the current year? Clearly we can't depend on the government to be the sole check to the overwhelming force of the dollar.

Data will not rescue us from capitalism run amok, but it can help by providing us with the knowledge we need to shine the spotlight on the major issues we face in our world. Government agencies, nonprofits, and concerned citizens alike can find, gather, and leverage data about:

- Environmental concerns such as climate change
- Infringements on our personal rights such as privacy violations
- Health crises such as chronic and infectious disease epidemics
- Human and civil rights abuses such as prejudice and violence

As we'll discuss later in the book, data is not without its imperfections. Just because someone produces data about a topic doesn't mean that the point of view is unassailable and immune from challenge. Data about our environment and societies is no different. Collecting and sharing data along with the information, knowledge, and wisdom gleaned from that data isn't the end of the journey, but a point along the road. There are other ways to see the data and other points of view to hear. We should approach data with a healthy degree of skepticism, but also with willingness to learn new truths—truths we must hold tentatively and be willing to revise or abandon in the face of future findings.

A good example of this is the famous "hockey stick graph," initially published in 1999 by Mann, Bradley & Hughes in their article "Northern Hemisphere Temperatures During the Past Millennium: Inferences, Uncertainties, and Limitations."[20] The following is a revision of the original 1999 graph created and published in 2013 by Klaus Bitterman (the original line is shown in blue):

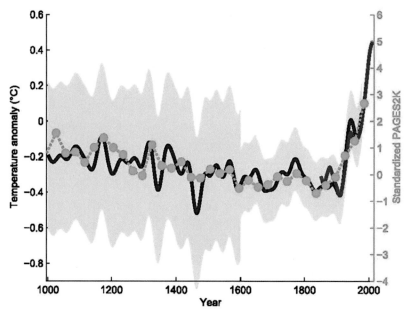

Figure 3.2. A revision of the "Hockey Stick Graph" by Klaus Bitterman (shared under CC4.0).[21]

This graph and its earlier version served as a wake-up call to many people across the world that our environment is undergoing an alarming change. This graph and the publications that went along with it were met with vigorous debate in the scientific community, but at present a

20. http://www.meteo.psu.edu/holocene/public_html/shared/research/ONLINE-PREPRINTS/Millennium/mbh99.pdf
21. https://en.wikipedia.org/wiki/File:T_comp_61-90.pdf

majority of publishing climate scientists seem to agree that anthropogenic, or human-caused, global warming is happening.[22]

Consensus isn't proof, but it's something to take very seriously. Unfortunately the topic has been politicized at present, at least in the United States. This has produced entrenched, value-based groups who depend on each other for economic and political strength as well as validation, making dialogue and progress very difficult. Leveraging data to improve our environment and our societies is not exactly a path strewn with rose petals.

But at least the data is available and accessible to all. This is thanks to the Open Data movement, which has its roots in the scientific research community, the open source software movement, and the notion of open government. The basic idea that these all share is that data about our world should be a common property, just like the air we breathe.

Another more recent example of public domain data having an enormous impact on the world arose during the COVID-19 Coronavirus pandemic that began in late 2019 and hit the world with unprecedented changes starting in early 2020, even as these words are typed. From the early stages of the disease, confirmed case counts and death counts by various levels of geography were widely and openly published by organizations such as Johns Hopkins Center for Systems Science and Engineering.[23]

News sites, governments, nonprofit organizations, and even citizen data explorers downloaded this data during the pandemic and created visualizations and forecasts about the spread as it propagated across the globe. One such organization is the UK education sector charity called Global Change Data Lab and their project "Our World in Data,"[24] based at Oxford University and led by Max C. Roser. Roser and his team published a variety of charts and graphs about the pandemic as it unfolded, including this semi-log plot showing the increase in COVID-19 deaths by country, saved on 13 April 2020:

22. https://climate.nasa.gov/scientific-consensus/
23. https://github.com/CSSEGISandData/COVID-19
24. https://ourworldindata.org/about

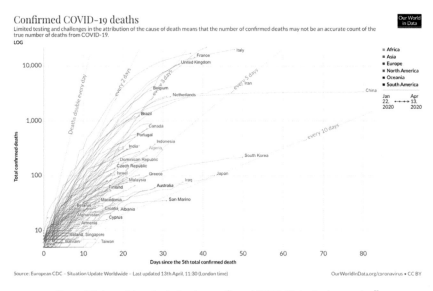

Figure 3.3. A semi-log chart showing confirmed COVID-19 deaths by country.[25]

The visualizations, analyses, and forecasts of the COVID-19 pandemic saw widespread distribution among citizens of many countries. Governing bodies used them to formulate plans to minimize the spread of the disease as well as its impact on their communities. This example underscores the importance of data in the public domain, as well as the level of data literacy that citizens of planet earth need to possess today.

Open public data doesn't only apply to the big problems in our world, though. All you have to do is search the internet for the "open data portal of {insert your city, state or country}." You will find a plethora of public data sets at the local, provincial, and national levels relating to routine and even sometimes quirky communal matters such as:

- At the city / community level (e.g. https://data.seattle.gov/):
  - City budgets and payroll
  - Building permit applications
  - Restaurant inspections
  - Test scores by school and district

25. Max Roser, Hannah Ritchie, and Esteban Ortiz-Ospina (2020). "Coronavirus Disease (COVID-19) – Statistics and Research." Published online at OurWorldInData.org. Retrieved from: https://ourworldindata.org/coronavirus.

- At the state / provincial level (e.g. https://data.wa.gov/):
  - Consumer complaints to the state Attorney General
  - State population by county and decade
  - Map of state libraries
  - Highest paid state employees

- At the federal / national level (e.g. https://www.data.gov/):
  - Campaign contributions to candidates
  - Storm events database and precipitation by hour
  - Federal student loan program data
  - Census data

These are just a tiny fraction of the data sets available to all of us. Government agencies and scientific organizations also make data freely available to the general public. There are even massive repositories of links to open data sites and sources such as the "Awesome Public Data-sets" Github repository created by Xiaming Chen.[26]

But as with reading books, the person who doesn't explore this data has no advantage over the person who can't.

EXERCISE 3.3: Search for an open data portal in the city, state, or country in which you live. Look for the page that allows you to explore the data sets that are available to you. List three different data sets that you think are interesting and would like to explore:

1. _____

2. _____

3. _____

---

26. https://github.com/awesomedata/awesome-public-datasets

Personal Domain

So far we have considered how data can help groups of people such as corporate teams, government agencies, communities, and societies get value out of data. But there's a third and final domain to consider: the individual. The teams and groups we form are only as strong as the people who make them up, so how can data help us in our personal lives?

There's a long history of humans using data to keep track of their life, to learn about themselves, and to improve their own personal outcomes. Long before the start of the Digital Revolution that began in the mid-1900s, and even long before bathroom scales became ubiquitous in the United States back in the 1910s, individuals were engaging in self-measuring and self-tracking.

In the *Autobiography of Benjamin Franklin,* written between 1771 and 1790, Franklin described his 13 moral virtues: temperance, silence, order, resolution, frugality, industry, sincerity, justice, moderation, cleanliness, tranquility, chastity, humility. He then went on to relate how he sought to make each of these virtues a personal habit by keeping track of offenses against each one in a book he marked up each night, upon reflecting on the day:

> *I made a little book, in which I allotted a page for each of the virtues. I ruled each page with red ink, so as to have seven columns, one for each day of the week, marking each column with a letter for the day. I crossed these columns with thirteen red lines, marking the beginning of each line with the first letter of one of the virtues, on which line, and in its proper column, I might mark, by a little black spot, every fault I found upon examination to have been committed respecting that virtue upon that day.[27]*

27. https://books.google.com/books?id=Y32wOLkDz1oC&pg=PA128

	S.	M.	T.	W.	T.	F.	S.
TEMPERANCE.							
EAT NOT TO DULLNESS; DRINK NOT TO ELEVATION.							
T.							
S.	*	*		*		*	
O.	**	*	*		*	*	*
R.			*			*	
F.		*			*		
I.			*				
S.							
J.							
M.							
C.							
T.							
C.							
H.							

Figure 3.4. A recreation of an example of Ben Franklin's virtue tracking journal.

Fast forward to today, and we live in a world with an amazing number of sensing devices all around us, on our wrists, in our pockets, sometimes even implanted within us. These devices can give us an estimate of how many steps we have taken, how far we have traveled, our heart rate, how long we slept last night, our blood glucose levels, and a dizzying number of other metrics. The possibilities to leverage personal informatics to adjust and improve our lives are many and varied.

The proliferation of sensors, the growth of data storage capacity, and the expansion of computing power to make sense of all that data have led to the recent rise of the Quantified Self movement. The term "quantified self" seems to have been proposed in San Francisco in 2007 by Gary Wolf and Kevin Kelly, editors of Wired

Figure 3.5. A GPS-enabled smart watch that tracks position, movement, and heart rate.

magazine.[28] Kelly had the following to say in a blog post on the topic:

> *Real change will happen in individuals as they work through self-knowledge. Self-knowledge of one's body, mind and spirit. Many seek this self-knowledge and we embrace all paths to it.*

Those involved in the Quantified Self movement didn't invent personal informatics or self-tracking (see also Lifelogging), but the movement has a twenty-first-century feel, with local meetups, conferences, an online forum, and a "Show and Tell" showcase where people share their own personal projects, methods, and learnings.[29]

Our era is characterized by a whole host of modern tracking means, from the sensing devices mentioned earlier that automatically collect data about our activities to more manual approaches such as apps like KeepTrack or online spreadsheets like Google Sheets that serve as a modern version of Benjamin Franklin's tables.

But in a world full of digital tools, the analog approach is still useful and popular. Data artists Giorgia Lupi and Stefanie Posavec wrote two books on the subject: *Dear Data* (Princeton Architectural Press, 2016) and *Observe, Collect, Draw!* (2018).

Figure 3.6. *Dear Data* and *Observe, Collect, Draw!* by Giorgia Lupi and Stefanie Posavec.

28. "What Is the Quantified Self?" by Kevin Kelly, October 5, 2007 https://www.webcitation.org/66TEY49wv
29. https://quantifiedself.com/show-and-tell/

In the first of these two books, *Dear Data,* Lupi and Posavec share the weekly correspondence that they carried out with each other via hand-drawn postcards, over the course of 52 weeks, between their respective homes in New York and London. Each week featured a different theme, from purchases they made to how often they used their phones to how often they smiled at strangers. Eight moleskine notebooks associated with their personal data correspondence project are now owned by the Museum of Modern Art (MoMA).[30]

Their second book, *Observe, Collect, Draw,* is a diary intended to help their readers start their "journey to the world of personal documentation." It includes a section of exercises to help you develop your own drawing style, followed by a series of 47 prompts that encourage you to collect and draw data about your sleeping habits, how music makes you feel, and your exercise or activity routine, to name a few.

Whatever you decide to measure and track, and whether you use sophisticated digital tools or a simple pad of paper and pen, tracking your life as seen through the lens of data is a good first step on your path to data literacy.

EXERCISE 3.4: The Quantified YOU

1. WONDER: Pick an aspect of your life. It can be anything you want: media consumption or sleep habits or your daily commute. Write a question that you have about that aspect of your life.

2. SEEK: Decide on a "SMART" metric (Specific, Measurable, Achievable, Relevant, and Time-bound) that can get you close to answering that question. Track that variable for the amount of time that will give you enough data to learn something interesting.

3. DISCOVER: Sketch the data values you have recorded on a sheet of paper in whatever way you find helpful and interesting. See if this process helps you turn the data into information and the information into knowledge.

30. https://www.moma.org/collection/works/215813

4. MATURE: Finally, decide what changes, if any, you will put into place so that you can turn the knowledge you have gleaned into wisdom.

Further Reading

https://thinkprogress.org/most-comprehensive-paleoclimate-reconstruction-confirms-hockey-stick-e7ce8c3a2384/

https://www.ted.com/talks/gary_wolf_the_quantified_self

https://quantifiedself.com/get-started/

https://www.liebertpub.com/doi/full/10.1089/big.2012.0002

https://www.amazon.com/Dear-Data-Giorgia-Lupi/dp/1616895322/

https://www.amazon.com/Observe-Collect-Draw-Visual-Journal/dp/1616897147/

Chapter 4

THE FOUR TYPES
OF DATA SCALES

"That which we call a rose by any other name would smell as sweet."
–Juliet, in Shakespeare's *Romeo and Juliet (II ii 1–2)*

In this world of ours, we are constantly surrounded by objects and situations to categorize, to count, and to measure. From a parent marking the height of a growing child on a doorpost to a business owner figuring out the level of sales and profit for a given month, each one of us spends time collecting and interacting with empirical data every single day.

These ways of capturing our reality, when put together, form the data sets we use to analyze what's happening so that we can make better decisions and grow in wisdom. They are brought together to form simple lists of items, or rows and columns in spreadsheets, or records and attributes in databases.

But is there only one way to measure the world, or are there many ways? Is every type of data value the same, or are there different types of data values? These questions involve turning data on itself: measuring and categorizing the systems of measurement and categorization. That's why they relate to the topic of "metadata," which, according to Merriam-Webster's, means "data that provides information about other data."[31]

---

31. https://www.merriam-webster.com/dictionary/metadata

Finding Common Ground

These are the very foundational questions that an American psychologist at Harvard named Stanley Smith Stevens was thinking about back in the middle of the twentieth century. Stevens had founded the Psycho-Acoustic Laboratory at Harvard, and he was busy trying to measure and study the subjective magnitude of an auditory sensation—in other words, how loud we as humans perceive sound. If you think about that endeavor, you can imagine how tricky it must have been. While it's easy enough for us to say whether a noise is louder than another noise, it's a different matter to say *how much louder*, or *how many times* as loud.

That's why Stevens and his colleagues were having so much difficulty working together to advance their field. In the early 1930s, they had formed a committee to try to agree on how to measure human sensations like this. They debated and argued for seven years, and ultimately they left their meetings no closer to consensus than they were when they started.

So on Friday, June 7, 1946, Stevens published an article in the 103rd volume of *Science* magazine titled "On the Theory of Scales of Measurement."[32] There he laid out a theory of measurement not just for psychoacoustics but for all of science and statistics, which has been widely adopted and also widely criticized. Let's consider his proposal, and also some alternate theories on the matter of how we measure. An understanding of this topic is core to developing data literacy.

Stevens proposed that there were four different data scale types: Nominal, Ordinal, Interval, and Ratio. This four-member typology forms the acronym NOIR, making it easier to remember as a bottle of pinot noir red wine.

These four types are often grouped into pairs. The first pair, Nominal and Ordinal, are often thought of as "Categorical" (or "Qualitative") because they involve separation into a limited number of discrete groups or categories that have distinct qualities. The second pair, Interval and Ratio, are often thought of as "Quantitative" (or "Numerical") because they are numbers that quantify what they represent and can be used in calculations:

32. https://psychology.okstate.edu/faculty/jgrice/psyc3214/Stevens_FourScales_1946.pdf

Figure 4.1. Two pairings of data scale types.

Additionally, quantitative data can either be discrete or continuous. Discrete data can take a finite number of quantities between two limits, such as counting coins or expressing a person's age in years. Continuous data can theoretically take an infinite number of quantities between two limits, such as the weight of the coins or the precise amount of time a person has lived, down to fractions of a second.

He also proposed that the type of scale into which a given measurement fell would dictate what statistics, such as averages or percentiles, could be legitimately used, and which could not be used. Let's consider these data scale types one by one.

1. Nominal Scales

The first scale type is the most basic. Nominal data scales are categorical variables that simply act as labels. The word "nominal" comes from the Latin word *nominalis,* which means "pertaining to a name or names," and that's just what they do. They allow us to distinguish between individual objects or groups of objects.

But they aren't limited to names in the traditional sense, like the name of a person or a company or a type of fruit. Nominal scales can actually include numbers, too, as on the back of a soccer player's jersey to help the referee tell who is who. They can also be combinations of numbers and letters, such as on a car's license plate.

words or letters only   numbers only   letters & numbers combined

Figure 4.2. Examples of nominal data scales: jersey numbers, fruit labels, license plates.

The values of nominal scales can refer to unique individuals, such as in the case of license plate numbers. States don't give the same license plate number to two different cars at the same time. Other times they refer to groups with multiple members, like vehicle type (truck, sedan, coupe, etc.). There can be multiple cases of each of these types of vehicle on the road or in a parking lot at any given time. Let's apply the data scale types to the following image as we go along:

Figure 4.3. Photo by Stephan Müller from Pexels.

What kind of analysis can we do with nominal scale values by themselves? The first type—unique identifiers—allows us to count the distinct number of individual cases:

Q. How many registered vehicles are in the parking lot?

A. There are 83 vehicles with unique license plates in the parking lot.

The second type of nominal variable—group or category names—allows us to count the members in each value of the nominal scale.

Q. How many white vehicles are in the parking lot?

A. There are 14 white vehicles in the parking lot.

EXERCISE 4.1: Name 2 more nominal scales that you can find in the parking lot photograph:

1. _____

2. _____

Note that there's no inherent notion of "greater than" or "less than" with nominal scales. We may have a favorite car color, but the name of the color itself simply distinguishes between different vehicles. The only two rules are that we can't give the same name to two different things (e.g. we can't say a car is both a red car and a blue car), and we can't give different names to things that are the same (e.g. we can't say that one gray car is gray and another gray car is white).

If we go back to our red wine mnemonic device for recalling Stevens's NOIR data scale typology, consider a cellar full of bottles of wine by type and vintage. What would be a good example of a nominal variable? Perhaps we could choose wine type: pinot noir versus cabernet sauvignon versus merlot, for example.

Interestingly, as captured poetically by Juliet's quote in the epigraph of this chapter, we can interchange any two values of a nominal scale and the purpose remains the same. If we all decided to call all roses skunks and all skunks roses, the new values would work just as well, as long as we swapped these words everywhere. As silly as that sounds, there are times when nominal values do change, like when a person changes their last name, or when a company gets acquired by a larger one.

Let's move on to the next scale to find a data scale type that captures the notion of order.

2. Ordinal Scales

The second categorical scale type is ordinal, which comes from the Latin word *ordinalis,* meaning "relating to order in a series," and that's just what they do: they tell us the order of the different levels of the scale. They also include the notion of equal or not equal to which nominal data scale types were limited.

For example, if we think of some competitions, perhaps those who compete can take home the gold, silver, or bronze medal in their category. These medal names aren't just different, they also have an inherent order to them. Gold is better than silver and silver is better than bronze.

Figure 44. An example of a three-tiered award, the Data Literacy Awards.

Values of ordinal scales can also be numbers, such as a rating from 0 to 5 that you might give to a product in a satisfaction survey (this is known as a Likert scale). By definition, 5 is better than 4, which is better than 3, and so on.

Ordinal scale values can also be letters, such as those given to the different levels of professional baseball leagues in the United States or the quality grade of a pearl (A, AA, AAA). The better players move up from A to AA to AAA, so there is an inherent order to the leagues that the letter scheme conveys.

Using the red wine mnemonic device once again, what's a good example of an ordinal variable that applies to our wine cellar? Certainly the rating of the wine, on a scale from 0 to 5. Or perhaps we have three different bottle sizes in the cellar: demi (small), standard (medium), and magnum (large). This would also be an ordinal variable, so long as we don't use the bottle volume itself, which we'll consider later.

EXERCISE 4.2: Let's go back to the parking lot photograph above (Figure 4.3). Name two different ordinal scales that you can find in the photograph. Feel free to use your imagination (e.g. the order in which they finished a race, or their place in a car show).

1. _____

2. _____

One interesting aspect of ordinal scales, if you think about it, is that the distances between successive levels of the scale aren't necessarily the same. What does this mean? Well, is the difference between a gold medal and a silver medal the same as the difference between a silver and a bronze medal? Not really. One could argue that the jump in value or worth from a silver medal to a gold medal is much larger than the jump from bronze to silver.

Similarly, if you rate a movie or a meal, there might be only a slight difference between a 3- and a 4-star rating, but the jump from 4 to 5 stars might be very significant. Another person's way of rating could be the opposite of that, and a 4 might be quite similar to a 5, while a drop from 4 to 3 stars might be a bigger deal to them. This system of numbering is subjective, and therefore not perfectly linear.

So we say that ordinal scales don't preserve the size of the intervals between successive values. That comes with the next scale.

3. Interval Scales

The third data scale type is the first quantitative one and forms the "I" in "NOIR," namely, the interval scale. Interval scales build on the first two scale types by preserving equality of intervals between successive levels of the scale. Points on the interval scale are equidistant from the next point.

Consider, for example, the temperature in the room in either Fahrenheit or Celsius. The difference between 10° and 20° is the same 10° difference that we have when we increase from 20° to 30°. Because of this property, addition and subtraction are all meaningful with interval scales.

An interesting property of the interval scale is that it doesn't have a "true" or absolute zero point. Instead, the zero point of an interval scale is a matter of convention or convenience, and it does not carry with it the notion of "none" or "nothing." Staying with our temperature example, 0°F and 0°C don't mean "no temperature." They're just a matter of convention. In the Celsius scale, 0°C was chosen as the point at which water freezes, but that doesn't mean there is a complete absence of temperature.

Other examples of interval scales include:

- Calendar year (There is no "zero" year; 1 BCE is followed by AD 1, and is arbitrary in any case)
- Location in coordinates (0 latitude and 0 longitude isn't "nowhere.")

EXERCISE 4.3: Interval scales can be more difficult to identify because of their need for an arbitrary zero, but see if you can go back to the parking lot photograph and identify at least one example of an interval scale (hint: think about car age or location).

1. _____

With our wine cellar example, maybe we have areas of the cellar held at different temperatures to optimize the aging of the different types of wine. That would be an interval scale. So would the wine vintage printed on the bottle label, indicating when the grapes were harvested.

Before introducing the fourth and final data scale type of Stevens's quartet, consider the following question: Is 20°C *twice as warm* as 10°C? It's not, is it? This type of operation is reserved for the most powerful quantitative scale type: ratio scale.

4. Ratio Scales

Ratio scales are the second quantitative scale type and the fourth and final scale type of the set of measurements outlined by Stevens. The difference between interval scales and ratio scales is that ratio scales have an absolute zero that does mean "none" or "nothing." With this main difference, ratio scales enable us to use multiplication and division in a meaningful way.

Let's take the example of the weight of a watermelon on a grocery store scale. Say a watermelon weighs 20 pounds. We can say that it is *four times as heavy* as a pineapple that weighs 5 pounds. And if we have no watermelon on the scale at all, it would read 0 pounds, so we are dealing with a quantitative scale that has an absolute zero.

We can also say that a watermelon that has grown from 10 to 15 pounds has *increased in weight by 50%*, or that it is now *150% of its previously measured weight,* or, *1.5 times as heavy*. These notions of percentage change and ratios now apply. We can't make similar statements about temperatures or calendar years, because they are interval scales.

If you think about it, the ratio scale incorporates the abilities of the other three scale types as well. As with interval scales, the equality of intervals applies: the difference in weight between a watermelon that weighs 20 pounds and one that weighs 25 pounds is the same as the difference between a 25- and a 30-pound watermelon. And as with ordinal scales, greater than and less than apply: a 21 pound watermelon is greater in weight than a 20 pound watermelon but less than one that weighs 22 pounds. And finally, as with nominal scales, determination of equality applies: a watermelon that weighs 21 pounds doesn't weigh the same as a 20 pound watermelon, but it does weigh the same as another 21 pound watermelon.

The following table summarizes these four scale types and their properties:

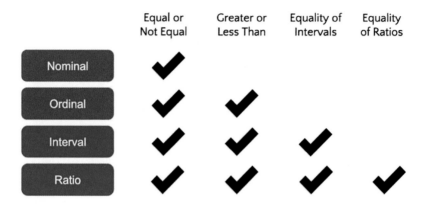

	Equal or Not Equal	Greater or Less Than	Equality of Intervals	Equality of Ratios
Nominal	✔			
Ordinal	✔	✔		
Interval	✔	✔	✔	
Ratio	✔	✔	✔	✔

Figure 4.5. The NOIR scale types and their properties.

Stevens pointed out that cardinal numbers—the scale we use when we count objects, such as when we counted the white vehicles in the parking lot—can be considered ratio scales. He also pointed out that ratio scales can either be "fundamental" or "derived." Fundamental ratio scales correspond to magnitudes such as length and weight that can be directly measured. Derived ratio scales, on the other hand, apply to magnitudes that are mathematical functions of fundamental magnitudes, such as density, which is mass divided by volume.

In our wine cellar example, if we return to the bottle size variable we considered in the ordinal scale section, what if we replaced the name of the bottle size with the volume of the bottle: 375ml for "Demi," 750ml for "Standard," and 1.5L for "Magnum." This would be a ratio variable type, as would the weight or cost of each bottle.

EXERCISE 4.4: Data that falls into ratio scales can be found everywhere. Go back to the image of the parking lot in Figure 4.3 and identify three different attributes of the objects in the photograph that can be measured using a ratio scale:

1. _____

2. _____

3. _____

As helpful as the NOIR typology is for people learning about data for the first time, it has its limitations. Let's consider some of the issues with this classification, and come up with some ways to use it and some ways to avoid using it.

Objections and Alternate Typologies

After the publication of Stevens's 1946 article, statistics textbook makers were quick to adopt the nominal, ordinal, interval, and ratio typology due to its simplicity and ease of explanation. But statisticians and practitioners since that time have raised objections to an overly strict application of this taxonomy in exploratory data analysis. These objections became all the more vociferous when statistical software packages started limiting what could be done with variables based on a rigid upfront determination of their scale type.

One early criticism made by Frederick Lord (1953)[33] is that numbers don't know or care what scale type they are. He told an amusing story of a fictional "Professor X" who was given the job of assigning jersey numbers to the players on the school soccer team. He knew that the jersey numbers were just nominal, and had no ordinal or quantitative meaning to them. So he was surprised when the freshmen came complaining that the sophomores were laughing at them because their jersey numbers were lesser than their own jersey numbers. How could he check whether this was true? The sophomores students' real world usage of the numbers to indicate "laughability" caused him to treat the jersey numbers as quantitative rather than nominal in his subsequent analysis.

So we can't apply scale types too rigidly. The scale often depends on the question being asked of the data rather than some innate property of the data itself.

33. https://psycnet.apa.org/record/2005-07821-008

Another criticism of Stevens's typology is that it doesn't exhaustively cover all common data types that we encounter in the real world. Consider, for example, percentages between 0% and 100%, such as the percent of executives in an industry who are women. What data scale type is this variable? It's a percentage that's determined by a fraction based on two cardinal, or counted, variables: the count of the number of women executives (the numerator) and the count of the total number of executives (the denominator).

Fractions, numerators and denominators

Example: 5 of a company's 8 executives are women

$$\text{fraction} = \frac{\text{numerator}}{\text{denominator}} = \frac{5}{8}$$

Figure 4.6. Fractions, numerators and denominators

Both of these values in the fraction can be considered ratio scales, but what about the fraction itself? We can also express this quotient as a fraction, a ratio (not to be confused with the scale type "ratio"), a proportion or a percentage:

Fractions, Ratios, Proportions & Percentages

Example: 5 of a company's 8 executives are women

Expressed...

As a fraction:	5/8	*"five eighths"*
As a ratio:	5:8	*"five to eight"*
As a proportion:	0.625	*"zero point six two five"*
As a percentage:	62.5%	*"sixty-two point five percent"*

Figure 4.6. Fractions, ratios, proportions and percentages

We'll consider percentages more in the next chapter.

Stevens's system doesn't account for other important data properties, such as whether a quantity is discrete (only able to take a finite list of values within a range, such as integers) or continuous (able to take an infinite number of values within a range, such as real numbers), or whether it can be less than zero. Statisticians Frederick Mosteller and John W. Tukey proposed an alternate list of data types in their 1977 work *Data Analysis and Regression: A Second Course in Statistics*:[34]

- Names
- Grades (eg. freshman, sophomore, junior, senior)
- Ranks (starting from 1, which can be the highest or lowest rank)
- Counted fractions (between 0 and 1, such as percentages)
- Counts (non-negative numbers)
- Amounts (non-negative real numbers)
- Balances (unbounded, positive, or negative numbers)

Ultimately, data is useful in that it helps us understand the world. It's a good idea to know as much as you can about the properties of the data you're using—its metadata—in order to appreciate how best to use it. It's also a good idea to remain open-minded about what the data means and how it can be used. You might find that a particular data variable yields insights that you didn't expect to get from it.

EXERCISE 4.5: The organizers of a Data Literacy meetup session are giving away raffle tickets to attendees as they walk in the door. The roll of tickets starts at #1 and goes up from there. You are given raffle ticket #41. The person sitting next to you has #35. At the end of the presentations, the organizers draw #81 as the lucky winner of the raffle. What data scale type is the raffle ticket in the following scenarios:

a.   You look at your ticket and realize that you haven't won the raffle.

b.   You realize that you arrived later than the person sitting next to you.

c.   The door greeter notices that the last raffle ticket she gave away was #126, meaning more than twice as many people attended this month's meetup than last month's.

34. https://www.pearson.com/store/p/data-analysis-and-regression-a-second-course-in-statistics/ P100000640139/9780201048544

EXERCISE 4.6: Go back to Exercise 3.4 and consider the variable you decided to track about your life. To what data scale type does it belong?

Further Reading

https://psychology.okstate.edu/faculty/jgrice/psyc3214/Stevens_FourScales_1946.pdf

Chapter 5

THE FIVE FORMS OF DATA ANALYSIS

"Analysis can tell us what is required, but it cannot make us act."
–Mary Frances Berry

In spite of how many organizations treat it, the purpose of collecting and gathering data isn't just to amass data for the sake of it. As we discussed in the first chapter, the purpose is to convert data into information, information into knowledge, and knowledge into wisdom.

But how does this happen?

In order to turn data into wisdom, we need to analyze it so that we can learn what it has to teach us. We can also use analytical techniques to anticipate what will happen next, and to help us chart a course forward. And then we can use data to measure the results, and to improve our approach for next time.

Of course, as we discussed in the third chapter, data and analysis can apply to the professional, public, or personal domain. And as we discussed in the second chapter, we can compare and contrast what our analysis tells us with what our intuition and experience tell us in order to develop a more complete picture. Remaining curious and skeptical about both of these systems of thought is a better approach than blindly trusting either of them while ignoring the other.

What's the difference between "analysis" and "analytics"? Analysis is a general term that refers to breaking down and examining the elements or structure of something. Analytics refers to the "discovery, interpretation, and communication of meaningful patterns in data."[35] Analytics also tends to specifically refer to more advanced machine learning techniques such as decision trees and neural networks.

In this chapter, we'll consider five different forms of data analysis: descriptive, inferential, diagnostic, predictive, and prescriptive. We'll see how these five forms successively increase in complexity and uncertainty, but also potentially in value and in the competitive advantage that they afford. That isn't to say that one form is better than the others. They each have their place and use, like different tools in a toolbox.

1. Descriptive	2. Inferential	3. Diagnostic	4. Predictive	5. Prescriptive
"What happened?"	"What about the rest?"	"What's going on under the surface?"	"What is likely to happen next?"	"What should we do about it?"

Figure 5.1. The 5 Forms of Data Analysis

1. Descriptive

Descriptive data analysis is the first type of data analysis we'll consider because it is the most basic and the most common. It's also the easiest form of data analysis in terms of technical difficulty.

Descriptive data analysis can provide us with information relevant to this question:

What happened in the past?

Using this approach, we focus on finding out what our data can tell us about the Who, What, When, and Where of our chosen topic of interest.

Sometimes the data we're using in our descriptive analysis is so recent that it feels more like it's answering the question "What's happening right now?" For example, we could be looking at a list of students who are all

35. https://en.wikipedia.org/wiki/Analytics

sitting in a classroom at this exact moment, or a report of all products physically located in a particular warehouse, right as a shift comes to an end.

Whether the data is about today, yesterday, or some other time in the past, this form of analysis promises to give us valuable information about our world. It just takes work to get it there, like mining any other valuable resource.

There are a number of common statistics we use when we seek to understand what our data is telling us. The branch of **descriptive statistics** gives us techniques to summarize a collection of data values so that we don't have to memorize the entire collection—something the human brain struggles to do as the size of the data set increases beyond even just a handful of values. As we'll see, calculating summary statistics is also one way to turn data into information.

Let's consider a number of different summary statistics one by one and see how we can use them to conduct descriptive data analysis. In order to do this, we'll consider a fictitious scenario, but one that uses real data.

Pretend you live in the South Lake Union neighborhood of the city of Seattle in the state of Washington in the United States. Your city has earned the nickname "Crane City," and you can see why—there are signs of construction everywhere.

In early November of 2018, you become curious about recent building permit applications for your neighborhood, loosely defined as the area within a one-mile radius of Lake Union Park.

Figure 5.2. Lake Union Park, Seattle.[36]

36. https://commons.wikimedia.org/wiki/File:Lake_Union_Park_(19569751209).jpg

You find a list of building applications submitted to the Seattle Department of Constructions and Inspections[37] for the first five days of the month of November and you decide to see what you can learn from it. Here's the table of permits submitted in the month so far:

Permit Num	Permit Class	Applied Date	Est Project Cost
6691497-CN	Commercial	11/1/18	$83,647
6697224-CN	Single Family/Duplex	11/2/18	$175,000
6697189-EX	Single Family/Duplex	11/2/18	$100,000
6688729-CN	Commercial	11/2/18	$70,000
6625505-CN	Single Family/Duplex	11/5/18	$336,392
6697498-CN	Commercial	11/5/18	$200,000
6697455-CN	Commercial	11/5/18	$3,000
6697438-BK	Commercial	11/5/18	$483,975

Table 5.1. A table of building permit applications for the South Lake Union area, 2018/11/1 to 11/5.

Counts

The simplest thing we can do with a list of items is to count them using the cardinal numbers we learned about in the previous chapter. There are a total of eight permit applications that appear in the table. Each has a distinct Permit Number that you can see in the first column. That's helpful to know, because in theory it's possible that a person might have submitted the same application twice.

This is a count of individual items or entities contained within the set. We can also count items grouped by one of the different data scale types:

- **Counts by Nominal variables:** We can count the number of unique items that fall into one of multiple categories, each with their own nominal variable name. For example, there are 5 applications that fall into the "Commercial" permit category, and 3 that fall into the "Single Family/Duplex" category.
- **Counts by Ordinal variables:** The second type of categorical variable is ordinal, the levels of which have an inherent order, as we've discussed. We don't have a variable like that in the table, but imagine if the table included a current status (scheduled,

37. https://data.seattle.gov/Permitting/Building-Permits/76t5-zqzr

additional info requested, closed) of the application. This categorical variable has an inherent order to it based on the process followed, and we could count how many of the eight applications are in each phase, just like we did with the nominal "Permit Class" variable.

- **Counts by Interval and Ratio variables:** When we move from the two categorical variables (nominal and ordinal) to the two quantitative ones (interval and ratio), we can still count items in the list. To do so, we would need to create "bins" out of successive ranges of the quantitative values. For example, notice the "Est Project Cost" column in Table 5.1. We can group all of the projects according to which bin their estimated project cost falls into as follows:

  - $0–$99,999: 3 applications (6697455-CN, 6688729-CN, 6691497-CN)
  - $100,000–$199,999: 2 applications (6697189-EX, 6697224-CN)
  - $200,000 and over: 3 applications (6697498-CN, 6625505-CN, 6697438-BK)

Minimum (Min) and Maximum (Max)

Every set of numbers with at least two different values has a maximum and a minimum. These are very straightforward statistics, but we focus on them a lot. For example, Table 5.1 has the following min and max for the "Est Project Cost" variable:

- **Minimum:** $3,000 (permit number 6697455-CN). This simply tells us the estimated project cost that is the smallest of the set.
- **Maximum:** $483,975 (permit number 6697438-BK). This simply tells us the estimated project cost that is the largest of the set.

Sums (Totals)

A very basic step in descriptive analysis is to add up any quantitative variables to give us an idea how much we are dealing with *in all.*

For example, if we add the eight estimated project costs together, we get a **total value** of **$1,452,014**. This tells us how much money builders in our neighborhood are projecting to spend on the eight most recent projects submitted to the city for approval.

Summing quantitative values is such a useful and common form of analysis. Companies sum up their sales amounts in months, quarters and years. Governments sum up the population of each census tract to determine the total population in the state or country. We sum up our income each year as a starting point to determine how much we owe in taxes, and so on.

Not every quantity is summed, though. Imagine if you weighed yourself on your bathroom scale each day for a month and kept the readings in a list. It wouldn't be very informative or meaningful to add up all the individual weight readings and say that your "total weight for the month" was 4,679 lbs.

Ratios, Proportions, and Percents

Once we determine counts and sums from our data, the next step is that we often want to figure out what *fraction of the total amount* a certain part or subset comprises. We can express this as a **ratio** (x out of y, or x:y), as a **proportion** (from 0 to 1) or as a **percent** (from 0% to 100%). It's a simple matter of dividing the part we're interested in with the total amount.

For example, let's consider the relationship between the number of commercial permit applications (5) and the total number of applications (8) in the first 5 days of November 2018:

- As a **ratio**: 5 commercial permit applications to 8 total applications = **5:8** or **5/8**
- As a **proportion**: 5/8 = **0.625**
- As a **percent**: 5/8 = 0.625 * 100% = **62.5%**

Since percent means "out of each hundred," we should avoid using this term when we're only dealing with a small number of cases. In this case, since there are only 8 permit applications in the list, saying that "62.5% of the applications are in the commercial class" is a bit misleading, because there are nowhere near 100 total cases. The good news is that we can fall back on proportions or ratios for situations with few cases.

Sometimes we find proportions less than 0 or greater than 1.0. Likewise, we can find percentages that are less than 0% or greater than 100%. In these cases we typically aren't comparing part to whole, but rather two completely different values, such as the number of applications last week to the number of applications this week (percent change), or the number of applications the department successfully processed in a week to our weekly goal (performance to plan). We'll consider these types of situations down the road.

Measures of Central Tendency

When we come across a set of numbers, we often want to know whether there's a number that's "typical" or "normal." These are fuzzy words, but essentially we're trying to put our finger on the center point of the values. In statistics, this is called central tendency.

The most common measure of central tendency is the average, but it's not the only one; there's also the median and the mode. Let's consider all three, and see what happens to each of them when we add more rows to our table above.

- **Mean:** The "arithmetic average," determined by adding all of the values and then dividing by the total number of values. For example, with the estimated project costs of our eight building permit applications, the mean would be:

Determining the Mean, or Average

$$\frac{\$83,647 + \$175,000 + \$100,000 + \$70,000 + \$336,392 + \$200,000 + \$3,000 + \$483,975}{8}$$

$$= \frac{\$1,452,014}{8}$$

$$= \$181,502$$

So applications submitted in the first five days of November 2018 involved projects that were estimated to cost an average of **$181,502**. The mean is often called the "representative value" because it's the single value that you could replace all of the values with and still get the same total if you summed them up.

- **Median:** Another way of determining a central value of your data is to find the median, or the middle value. In order to find the middle value, we line up all of the values in ascending or descending order, and we take the one in the middle. If there are 9 values, we pick the 5th largest, which will have 4 less than or equal to it and 4 that are greater than or equal to it. Any set with an odd number of values has a single value in the middle.

  If there are 8 values, like in our data set, or any even number of values, there is no single value in the middle. Instead, there are two in the middle—the 4th and the 5th in our case. So, to determine the median where there's an even number in the set, we find the average, or mean, of the middle two values by adding them together and dividing by two. This gives us a median estimated project cost for the first 5 days of November in our neighborhood of **$137,500**:

Determining the Median, or 50% Percentile

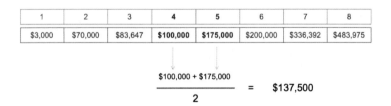

1	2	3	4	5	6	7	8
$3,000	$70,000	$83,647	$100,000	$175,000	$200,000	$336,392	$483,975

$$\frac{\$100,000 + \$175,000}{2} = \$137,500$$

- **Mode:** The mode is simply the value that occurs the most often in the set of values. In our small table with eight rows, no single estimated project cost appears more than once, so there is no mode. This is often the case with continuous data, where there's a good chance that each value in the set is different from all of the others.

Say, for example, we're interested in understanding the median age (in years) of the people who attend an event. Perhaps there are 25 people in the room. Seven of them happen to be 32 years old, and the next most common age, 28, only applies to six people at the event. In that scenario, 32 would be the mode. What happens if a 26th person shows up late, and that person is 28 years old? Now we have two modes—there are seven people who are 32 years old and seven people who are 28 years old.

In the next chapter, we'll see how visualizing this kind of data set can help us analyze it even better.

Central Tendency, Revisited

Let's take another look at the difference between mean, median, and mode when we add new data, and see how these statistics change in response to the addition. If we waited one more day to collect data about permit applications, we'd add two more rows to our table because a ninth and a tenth application for the month were submitted on November 6:

Permit Num	Permit Class	Applied Date	Est Project Cost
6691497-CN	Commercial	11/1/18	$83,647
6697224-CN	Single Family/Duplex	11/2/18	$175,000
6697189-EX	Single Family/Duplex	11/2/18	$100,000
6688729-CN	Commercial	11/2/18	$70,000
6625505-CN	Single Family/Duplex	11/5/18	$336,392
6697498-CN	Commercial	11/5/18	$200,000
6697455-CN	Commercial	11/5/18	$3,000
6697438-BK	Commercial	11/5/18	$483,975
6697738-EX	Multifamily	11/6/18	$17,000,000
6694765-PH	Commercial	11/6/18	$460,000,000

Table 5.2. An updated list with two new applications to consider.

Notice that these projects are estimated to cost far more than the previous eight. The tenth application is for the complete renovation of a sports arena that's not far from where you live. With these two new rows added, we can recalculate the mean and the median of our set:

- The new mean = $47,845,201 (recall that the previous mean was $181,502)
- The new median = $187,500 (recall that the previous median was $137,500)

Notice how the mean increases a great deal more when we add the two new cases, which are "outliers" compared to the rest, meaning that they're significantly different in size.

The reason that the mean increases so much more than the median is that because the mean requires us to add up all the cases, so any outliers will have a large impact on the sum. In contrast, the median just requires us to line up the values and find the middle one. If we add a new maximum value to the set, it doesn't matter whether it's barely larger than the previous maximum, or many times larger; the effect on the median is the same.

This is an important point, and it's why we often use median when we talk about home prices or salary or net worth. Variables like these tend to have extreme values, unlike human height or weight, where extreme outliers don't occur to the same degree.

Measures of Dispersion

Once we get a handle on where a particular set of values is centered, the next question that arises is how much are the individual values spread out? Let's use two different measures of dispersion to find out:

- **Range:** The range is simply the difference between the maximum and the minimum values:

  ○ For the first eight applications: $483,975 - $3,000 = $480,975
  ○ For the first ten applications: $460,000,000 - $3,000 = $459,997,000

  This tells us the difference, or the gap, between the smallest and the largest estimated project cost.

- **Standard Deviation:** The standard deviation is a measure of the variation of the values in the set. If a standard deviation is low, that means that the individual values are grouped close to the mean. On the other hand, if a standard deviation is high, that means the values are spread out far away from the mean.

EXERCISE 5.1: You run a meetup group of small business owners and entrepreneurs, and you want to encourage existing members to invite new attendees who are just getting started with their first small business.

Figure 5.3. A photo from your small business meetup group session.[38]

You asked attendees at your latest monthly meeting fill out a sign-in sheet and had them write down their first name, their attendee type (member or visitor), and the number of years of experience running their own small business:

Name	Attendee Type	Years of Experience	Name	Attendee Type	Years of Experience
Giorgia	Member	12	Andy	Visitor	2
Alberto	Member	6	Steve	Visitor	4
Enrico	Member	7	Sarah	Visitor	3
Robert	Member	3	Jordan	Visitor	1
Hannah	Member	25	Valerie	Visitor	3
Cheryl	Member	5	Jane	Visitor	6
RJ	Member	8			
Santiago	Member	7			

Table 5.3. Attendance from the most recent monthly meeting of your small business group.

Based on the tables entered into your spreadsheet software, determine the following:

38. Photo by NeONBRAND on Unsplash

- Counts:
  - The total **count** of attendees
  - The **count** by attendee type

- Min & Max:
  - The **minimum** number of years of experience of attending members
  - The **maximum** number of years of experience of the visitors

- Sums:
  - The **total** years of experience of the members in attendance
  - The **total** years of experience of all attendees

- Ratios, Proportions, and Percents:
  - The **ratio** of members to visitors
  - The **proportion** of attendees who are not members
  - The **percentage** of attendees who are members

- Measures of Central Tendency:
  - The **mean** (average) years of experience of members in attendance
  - The **median** years of experience of visitors
  - The **mode** of the years of experience of members in attendance

- Measures of Dispersion:
  - The range of years of experience of all attendees
  - The standard deviation of years of experience of members

2. Inferential

Inferential data analysis is similar to descriptive data analysis in that it's primarily concerned with what happened in the past, but it's different in that it involves not just the data we have, but also the data we don't have.

To "infer" is to "to derive as a conclusion from facts or premises.[39]" Synonyms of "infer" include "deduce," "surmise," and "guess." The process involves some reasoning from the known to the unknown.

---

39. https://www.merriam-webster.com/dictionary/infer

Inferential Data Analysis seeks to answer this question:

What about the rest?

What does this mean? When is this sort of analysis necessary or helpful? Inferential analysis comes into play any time it's impractical or even impossible to collect data from every single member of some population.

This can occur when, for example, it would cost too much money or take too long to collect data from every single member of a population. Think about trying to poll every single person in your home state or province. Other times, the population is hypothetical or unknown, such as all of the eventual users of a prescription drug that hasn't yet been released to the market. We can't know ahead of time who will use the drug down the road.

Inferential statistics seeks to inform statements about a *population* based on data obtained from a *sample* of that population:

- A **population** is any group of individual members that have at least one trait in common. Members of the population could have any trait in common, or possibly many traits in common, depending on what you're interested in understanding. For example, you could be trying to learn about all of the people who purchased a certain product, or all of the first-year engineering students at a university, or all of the drivers in a state with blue eyes. You define the criteria.

- A **sample** is a smaller number of observations taken from the total that makes up the population. Let's say that 10,000 customers have purchased a specific product, but we can't reach out to all of them. We could survey 5,000 or 1,000 or 250 or even 2. These groups would all be samples of the population. In general terms, the larger the sample, the more confidence we can have in our inferences about the population.

With statistical inference, we're ultimately trying to estimate some parameter of the population; maybe it's satisfaction level, or height, or whatever. To do so, we collect data from a sample, and we compute a statistic of that sample. Populations have parameters, and samples have statistics: This is how we generalize from the few to the many:

- **P->P:** Populations (the "many") have **parameters** (e.g. the average height of all Canadian adults)
- **S->S:** Samples (the "few") have **statistics** (e.g. the average height of 1,000 randomly chosen Canadian adults)

Let's consider a few more examples. Customer satisfaction surveys are a common place where analysts make inferences with data. Only a portion of the total number of customers are surveyed. Of those who are sent the survey, sometimes only a portion actually respond. How are we to know how closely the survey responses we managed to collect reflect the feelings of the whole population? In this example:

- The population: All of our customers that meet a certain criterion or set of criteria
- The parameter: The median satisfaction score of all customers
- The sample: The customers who replied to the email survey
- The statistic: The median satisfaction score of the survey respondents

Another example of collecting data from samples rather than the entire population is destructive quality control testing. In these types of tests in a manufacturing environment, products are destroyed in some way in order to collect data about how well they're being built. For example, quality engineers take a small number of mobile phones from a production line each day and drop them from a certain height onto a concrete floor. Do they crack or break or not? If they destroyed each and every unit that was made, they wouldn't have anything left to sell. How are they to estimate the overall level of quality of the entire batch of phones if they're only looking at data from a sample? In this example:

- The population: All of the phones produced on a manufacturing line
- The parameter: The percent of phones that would survive a drop of 5 feet

- The sample: The units taken from each lot to destroy in testing to check quality
- The statistic: The percent of test units that actually do survive a drop of 5 feet

In these situations, we use **statistical inference** to analyze our data, draw conclusions, and make decisions. In this section we'll cover some important topics related to inferential data analysis, but we won't go as far as replicating an entire introductory statistics course. The emphasis is on understanding the key concepts as opposed to performing statistical hypothesis tests. In Data Literacy Level 2, we cover how to perform certain kinds of statistical tests of this type.

The characteristics of the sample are very important, and can have a huge impact on whether or not our inference is valid.

Sample Size

The sample size, often referred to as "n," is the number of observations taken from the population. If 250 people reply to our customer satisfaction survey, then n = 250.

When scientists, statisticians, and analysts design an experiment or create a data collection plan, they often need to take sample size into careful consideration. In general, the larger the sample size, the more closely we can infer the value of a parameter from the statistic of the sample. If you only survey 4 patients at a hospital, how much can you really say about the experience of all 7,000 outpatient visitors seen that week? What about if you survey 400 patients?

If someone is communicating findings from data taken from samples and they don't tell you the sample size, you should ask for it. If the sample size is small, you should be wary of the conclusions they're trying to make.

Population Size

The population size is just that: the total number of members in the population. When we talk about the population, we're not just talking about the number of people who live somewhere. The members of this type of population could be persons, events, things. As mentioned before, they all have at least one trait in common.

If the data set includes data about *every single one* of the members of the population, then it is called a **census**. An example of a census is the one conducted by the United States Federal Government every ten years (a "decennial" census), in which every person living in the United States as well as five U.S. territories are counted.

> **Barack Obama on Twitter:** *It's Census Day and we all have a crucial role to play. Filling out the 2020 Census determines what the next decade will look like for your community: your roads, health care, schools, representation and more. Takes a few minutes by mail, phone or online.*

Representative Samples

When choosing a sample of a population from which to collect data, a primary goal is to define a sample that's **representative** of the overall population. By "representative," we mean that the sample accurately reflects the traits of the larger population.

One way of seeking to achieve representativeness is with a simple random sample (SRS), in which each member of the population is given an equal likelihood of being included in the sample.

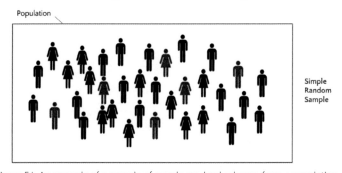

Figure 5.4. An example of a sample of people randomly chosen from a population.

This can lead to sampling error, though, when one subgroup is randomly selected more often than another.

Stratified sampling is commonly used in nation-wide polls and surveys. In this method, researchers select a sample that directly reflects specific chosen population characteristics. For example, if researchers know that 45% of a population are males, then they can make sure that 45% of their sample are males. They can similarly stratify their sample based on other traits, such as geographic location or political affiliation.

Biased Samples

It's critically important that the sample selected is **representative** of the population. We can't learn anything about retirees in Russia if we survey students in Sri Lanka. That may be an egregious example, and it may seem obvious, but there are far more elusive ways that samples fail to represent the intended population.

Bias can be introduced in many different ways. Bias exists whenever the sample from which you draw data has some systematic difference from the overall population. You might not think your sample is biased, but if you simply select based on ease of access or degree of familiarity, you might be choosing members that look a lot like you:

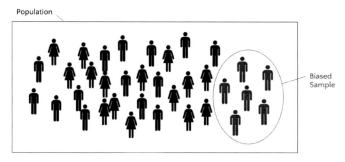

Figure 5.5. An example of a biased sample where those chosen look a lot alike.

Here are two common types of sampling bias to be aware of and to seek to eliminate when forming samples to measure:

- Undercoverage Bias: Undercoverage happens any time a segment of the population is less likely to be included in the sample than other segments. If you want to poll the members of a group about what time meetings should begin, you can't just survey members prior to the start of a meeting one day and only ask those who show up early. You'd be leaving out the members who arrived on time or late, and they might have a very different opinion about when future meetings should start.

A famous example of undercoverage bias occurred in 1948 when Democratic nominee Harry Truman, the incumbent, ran against Republican nominee Thomas Dewey for the presidency of the United States. Three major polls indicated that Dewey would win by a healthy margin, prompting the *Chicago Tribune* to print a headline the night of the election with the infamous title "Dewey Defeats Truman." Of course the opposite happened, and Truman gleefully held aloft the printed paper, proclaiming, "That ain't the way I heard it."

Figure 5.6. Harry Truman after he was declared the winner of the 1948 election.[40]

When the polls were revisited, it was discovered that Democratic voters had been underrepresented in the polls due to the fact that the data had been collected via telephone. In 1948, telephones were still not in every household, with affluent families more likely to have one than poorer families. And Democratic voters

40. https://commons.wikimedia.org/wiki/File:Dewey_Defeats_Truman_(AN-95-187)_resized.jpg

were less likely to be affluent, therefore less likely to own a telephone, and therefore less likely to be included in the polling data.

- Self-Selection Bias: When members of a group, typically people in this case, are able to decide whether or not to participate in the poll, survey, or other data collection plan, then a source of bias can arise. This bias can be severe when the motivation to participate or not is closely related to the characteristic being measured.

For example, if we want to understand whether people using a bathroom think it is clean, a tactile voting means at the restroom exit won't produce a representative sample. Those who found the bathroom to be unsanitary might be less likely to want to touch the buttons on the panel than those who found it very clean, leading to a higher statistic (say, median satisfaction level) for the sample than the actual parameter of the population:

Figure 5.7. A voting panel at the exit of an airport restroom that suffers from self-selection bias.

3. Diagnostic

Diagnostic Data Analysis goes beyond knowing what happened (Descriptive) and deriving conclusions about a population (Inferential), and involves uncovering unknown or hidden factors that lie beneath the surface of the original outcome you observed.

"Diagnosis" is defined in the dictionary as "investigation or analysis of the cause or nature of a condition, situation, or problem."[41] With data analysis, diagnosis involves looking beyond the initial observation, drilling down into categories, looking for anomalies, or comparing the data you have with other data not included at first.

Like a doctor who examines a patient in order to discover the nature of the disease that is producing the symptoms, Diagnostic Data Analysis seeks to answer this question:

What's going on under the surface?

Often people claim that Diagnostic Data Analysis answers the question *"Why is it happening?"* but this is treading on dangerous ground, as we'll consider later. The adept analyst must remain skeptical about their own findings, and avoid the temptation to jump to the conclusion that they've discovered the true underlying cause or causes of phenomena. There are often other explanations or lurking factors of which they are not aware.

Diagnostic Data Analysis involves a number of different approaches. The experienced analyst knows that every situation and every data set is different, but like the crime scene investigator who has a playbook of do's and don'ts, analysts have a few common techniques they use to their advantage:

Drilling Down

As we discussed in the previous chapter, our data often includes categorical variables such as gender or color or nationality. These categories can sometimes combine with other categories found in the data to form

---

41. https://www.merriam-webster.com/dictionary/diagnosis

hierarchies. A **hierarchy** is defined as "any system of persons or things ranked one above another."[42] Some examples of hierarchies include:

- Places grouped into countries, states, counties, and cities.
- Time grouped into years, months, weeks, and days.
- Employees grouped into business units, departments, and teams.
- Products grouped into families, classes, types, and items.
- Athletes grouped into leagues, conferences, divisions, and teams.

The following diagram shows an example of a hierarchical structure within a business unit. Employees at the company work on different teams, the different teams are grouped into different departments with no overlap, and those departments in turn fall under the business unit as a whole:

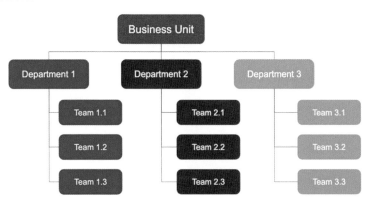

Figure. 5.8. A simple example of a hierarchy of working groups in a business.

"Drilling down" involves moving from a summary or aggregate level view of the data to a more granular or specific view of the data at a lower level of the hierarchy. "Drilling up" (sometimes called "reverse drill down") is the opposite, and involves shifting focus from the specific to the general by moving to a higher level of the tree.

A simple example of this would be to consider the topic of deforestation. The World Bank provides data about the total square kilometers

42. https://www.dictionary.com/browse/hierarchy

of forest area by country and year.[43] We can use this data to find out the change in forest area from 2015 to 2016.

If we do that, we'll discover with just a little bit of arithmetic that the world lost a reported 33,059 square kilometers of forest over that year. That's a little more than the entire area of the U.S. state of Maryland.

The data set includes forest area data for each country, and we can add the geographic regions of each country to create a hierarchy like the one shown in Figure 5.9: the world at the top can be divided into regions at the second level, and the regions can be divided into countries at the bottom. Each country is in one and only one geographic region, so the hierarchy is complete.

If we "drill down" from the global level at the top to the regional level at the next level down, we'll find that some regions of the world lost forest area between 2015 and 2016, such as Sub-Saharan Africa (-28,461 sq. km) and Latin America and Caribbean (-21,764 sq. km). On the other hand, some regions of the world actually gained in forest area over this time, such as Europe and Central Asia (+4,922 sq. km) and East Asia and Pacific (+8,462 sq. km), as shown in Figure 5.9:

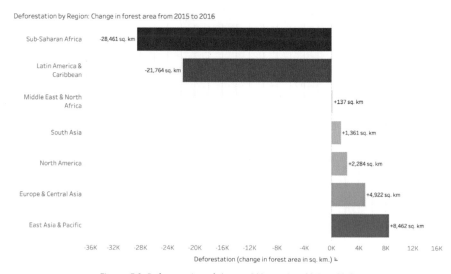

Figure. 5.9. Deforestation of the world by region, 2015 to 2016.

43. https://data.worldbank.org/indicator/AG.LND.FRST.K2

We could continue to drill down from the region level to the country level, the third level of the hierarchy. This would help us "diagnose" what happened at the lowest level for which there is data available. Doing so would reveal, for example, that while the Latin America and Caribbean region certainly had countries like Brazil (-9,840 sq. km) and Paraguay (-3,254 sq. km) that lost significant amounts of forest area, it also had other countries like Chile (+3,008 sq. km) and Cuba (+536 sq. km) that actually increased in forest area.

If our goal was to reduce deforestation, we'd certainly handle these countries very differently. Thus "drilling down" can help analysts and decision makers peel back the layers of the onion and so avoid the mistake of overgeneralizing. On the flip side of that coin, "drilling up" can help us see the bigger picture, and thereby avoid missing the forest for the trees.

Finding Correlations

Often Diagnostic Data Analysis involves comparing two different quantitative variables to find out if they're related in any way. In the last section on "drilling down," we considered different *categorical* variables that formed a hierarchy. In this section, we'll consider different *quantitative* variables at the same time to see if any relationship between them exists.

We'll consider more ways to visualize data in the next chapter, but a quick overview of the Cartesian coordinate system will help us come to a better understanding of correlation. The following figure shows an example of the Cartesian coordinate system, which is defined as:

A system in which the location of a point is given by coordinates that represent its distances from perpendicular lines that intersect at a point called the origin. A Cartesian coordinate system in a plane has two perpendicular lines (the x-axis and y-axis).[44]

---

44. https://www.dictionary.com/browse/cartesian-coordinate-system

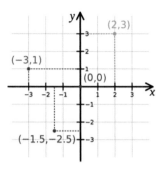

Figure 5.10. An example of the Cartesian coordinate system.[45]

It's called "Cartesian" after René Descartes, a French mathematician and philosopher who published the idea in 1637. It's very useful for comparing two quantitative variables in a data set because it allows us to see with our eyes whether any relationships exist, and how strong those relationships might be.

It's possible for two quantitative variables to be related in different ways illustrated in Figures 5.11 and 5.12. We've used the Cartesian coordinate system to plot one of the variables on the horizontal axis, often called the x-axis, and the other on the vertical axis, often referred to as the y-axis. Then, we've drawn a best-fit line, also called a regression line, that minimizes the distance between the line and all of the points in each of the plots.

In the first diagram, we see the difference between variables that have:

- A **positive correlation** (the best-fit line has a positive slope that *rises* from left to right),
- A **negative correlation** (the best-fit line has a negative slope that *falls* from left to right), and
- **No correlation** at all (the best-fit line is nearly horizontal and has a slope very close to 0).

45. https://commons.wikimedia.org/wiki/File:Cartesian-coordinate-system.svg

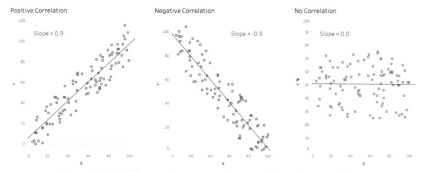

Figure 5.11. The difference between positive, negative, and no correlation.

Additionally, it's possible for the correlation between two variables to have varying degrees of strength. We use a term called R^2 (or R-Squared, or R^2) to determine how strong two quantitative variables are correlated. R^2 is called the "**coefficient of determination**," and it can range from 0 to 1.0, sometimes expressed as 0% to 100%.

- A **weak correlation** (either positive or negative) is one in which the points lie relatively far away from the best-fit line, and R^2 would be a relatively smaller number, closer to 0.

- A **strong correlation** is one in which the points lie very close to the best-fit line, and R^2 would be closer to 1.0.

- A **perfect correlation** is one in which the points lie exactly on the best-fit line, and this type of correlation has a R^2 of 1.0:

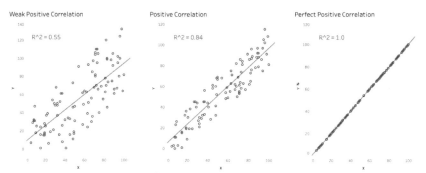

Figure 5.12. Different levels of strength of correlations.

So far we've just considered random dots on plots, so let's consider an example using real data to make the concept more meaningful.

If we want to understand whether there is a relationship between the percent of people living in an urban environment and the life expectancy of people born in different countries of the world, we can plot these two variables on a Cartesian plane as follows:

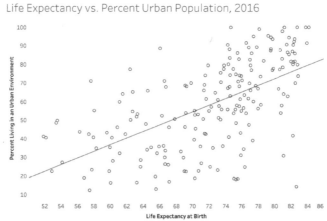

Figure 5.13. A scatter plot of life expectancy versus urbanization by country.

The trend line shows a statistically significant relationship between these variables, but the correlation is weak. The best-fit regression line has an R^2 of 0.348. Generally, in social sciences, an R^2 of between 0.25 and 0.64 is considered a moderate correlation.[46]

We can size the ring by country population and color them based on their region, yielding the bubble chart shown in Fig 5.14.

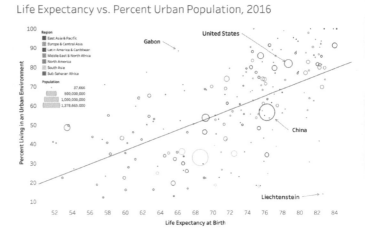

Figure 5.14. A bubble chart that adds population and region to the view.

46. http://psychology.okstate.edu/faculty/jgrice/psyc3214/Ferguson_EffectSizes_2009.pdf

What does this mean, though? Are we to understand that one variable causes the other to some degree? If so, which causes which? Does living longer somehow cause people to want to move into the city, or does living in the city somehow cause people to live longer?

We can't say either of these statements are true based on the data alone. One could cause the other, or vice versa, or something else entirely might be causing both of them. This is why it's dangerous to think of Diagnostic Data Analysis as answering the question "Why?" It often doesn't do that. Instead it points to new, more important questions by virtue of the fact that it uncovers interesting relationships in the data.

You may have heard the phrase "Correlation does not imply causation." This is an important phrase to consider at this point. What exactly does it mean? It means that just because two variables are correlated, it does not necessarily mean that one causes the other, or vice versa. There may be one or more other variables, called confounders or "lurking" variables, that are behind the relationship.

Would you believe that monthly rat sightings in New York City are correlated moderately well with building permit applications in Seattle? It turns out that the data shows that they are fairly well correlated ($R^2 = 0.48$).

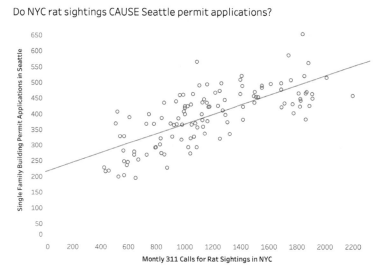

Figure 5.15. Correlation between NYC rat sightings and building permit applications in Seattle.

Do rat sightings in New York City somehow cause people to apply for building permits in Seattle? Or do applications for building in Seattle somehow cause people in New York City to call more often to complain about rats? Of course you can imagine that there's no way that either variable directly causes the other. Then what could be going on here?

We'll leave it at that for now and see if we can uncover another clue about what might be happening later in the section on predictive analytics.

Spotting Outliers

A key element of diagnostic data analysis involves looking for anomalies and data values that are significantly different than the rest. These values are often known as "outliers."

For example, if we were to consider the history of daily complaints to the New York City 311 call center for rat sightings, we would see the following dot plot over time:

Reported NYC Rat Sightings by Day

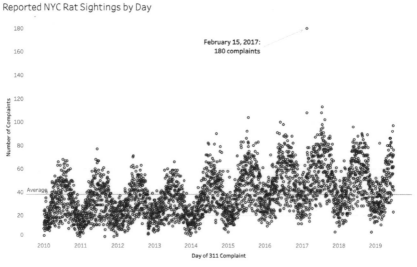

Figure 5.16. Dot plot of reported NYC rat sightings by day.

It's difficult not to notice the day that received 180 complaints for rat sightings: February 15, 2017. This day in history was definitely an outlier in at least this one respect. The average number of calls received per day for rat sightings over this period is just 38, so that one day saw almost 5 times as many calls. Why might that have happened?

While the data and the dot plot reveal an interesting outlier, they don't necessarily explain *why* it happened. A simple internet search for the phrase "New York rat sightings February 15, 2017" gives us an interesting clue, though.

This was the very day that a number of news organizations, including the *New York Times,* ran an article about a rare bacterial infection called leptospirosis that people can contract from coming into contact with rats. The *New York Times* headline: "Rare Disease Strikes a Bronx Area All Too Familiar With Rats."[47]

Could these articles be connected to the flood of calls? We'd need to talk to the phone operators to know for sure, but it seems like that's a plausible explanation. We wouldn't have known about the outlier without the data, and we wouldn't have known to ask the question about February 15, 2017. So the data set was a key part of our investigation. But the data itself wasn't able to take us all the way to find the culprit.

4. Predictive

Predictive Data Analysis involves using historical data to make predictions about future outcomes. This can be a very powerful technique, but there's no denying that it's tricky business. Any prediction made needs to come with a rather prominent asterisk, as we'll see in this section.

Predictive Data Analysis seeks to answer the question:

What's Likely to Happen Next?

But how can data collected yesterday help us project what's going to happen tomorrow? The answer is that data often reveals interesting trends and patterns that we can use to create models to predict the future.

---

47. https://www.nytimes.com/2017/02/15/nyregion/bronx-ny-rat-disease.html

Spotting Trends

If we apply a linear regression model that we introduced in our study of correlation to time series data, then we can identify trends that help us predict the future.

Consider a fictional scenario in which you are running a series of monthly webinars for your company. You have been keeping track of how many people attend each webinar, and you'd like to know if your efforts to promote the events have been bearing fruit.

On the x-axis, you plot the event number, a proxy for time since events are spaced a month apart. On the y-axis, you plot the number of attendees for each event. You then use linear regression to find that the data you collected matches most closely to a straight line that increases at a rate of 16 people per event: $y = 16x + 324$:

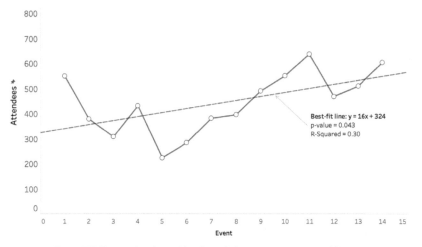

Figure 5.17. Time series data with a best-fit linear regression trend line

Note that showing time going from left to right on the horizontal axis like this is a very common convention when visualizing change over time.

We see that the coefficient of determination, R-Squared, is small (0.30), meaning that the event number accounts for about 30% of the observed variation in attendance. Recall from the previous section of this chapter that if the event number were a better predictor of attendance, then R-Squared would be closer to 1, and the dots would lie closer to the best-fit line.

We see another statistic in the best-fit line annotation box, though: p-value. What does this statistic mean, and how can we use it? Much has been written about the often confusing notion of the p-value. It is not a simple concept to grasp, and even experts often struggle to explain it.[48]

Before we talk about p-value, though, we need to mention two related concepts: the null hypothesis and the alternative hypothesis. The null hypothesis corresponds to the scenario in which there's no relationship between the two variables. With linear regression, if the null hypothesis were actually true, we'd expect to see a best-fit line that's pretty close to flat, or horizontal (slope = 0). The alternative hypothesis is that there is a relationship between the two variables, and the best-fit line wouldn't be flat; it would have some slope to it. We use the data we collected to conduct a hypothesis test to find out whether or not it's reasonable to reject the null hypothesis.

In simple terms, we use the p-value to determine the probability that we would get results *at least as extreme as the ones we observed, assuming the null hypothesis is true*. In other words, in our example, if there were no relationship at all between the event number and the attendance, then how likely is it to get a slope for our best-fit line that's at least as steep as the one we actually got?

The p-value is low (0.043), so the probability of getting a slope that's at least as steep as the one in our chart is low. Most statisticians would use a result like this to reject the null hypothesis, and to move forward assuming that there is, in fact, a statistically significant relationship between the two variables.

Many times a p-value of 0.05 is used as a cut-off point for establishing statistical significance. This cut-off is referred to the critical value or the alpha level. The null hypothesis would then be rejected for p-values below 0.05, and p-values above 0.05 mean that the test fails to reject the null hypothesis. It's important to note that a critical value of 0.05 is arbitrary, and blindly using this as a litmus test for statistical significance can be dangerous.

---

48. https://fivethirtyeight.com/features/not-even-scientists-can-easily-explain-p-values/

Another way that analysts seek to answer whether the data includes a statistically significant trend (either increasing or decreasing) is using statistical process control. Using this method, data such as we've collected would be plotted on an individuals chart, and statistical rules would be applied to determine whether observed variation amounts to signals or noise. One way of looking for significant trends is to look for any run of six consecutive points that are all increasing or all decreasing:

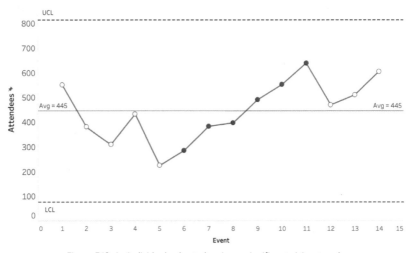

Figure 5.18. An individuals chart showing a significant rising trend

In this case, we can see that after our fifth event, we saw a streak of six events in a row where the attendance went up. This would constitute a signal in the data, and it would serve as a flag that there's a good chance the observed trend didn't just happen by chance.

Identifying Patterns

There are many different kinds of patterns that a particular data set can form. Sometimes a single data set includes multiple patterns within it. A pattern is simply any regularity in the world that allows us to create a model that approximates the observed behavior. A common pattern to which we can all relate is seasonality.

Seasonality can be said to exist any time a data set's pattern is related to the calendar year and that repeats over a one-year period.

When we consider the calls to complain about rats in New York City, a line chart of the number of calls over time reveals an interesting wave-shaped pattern:

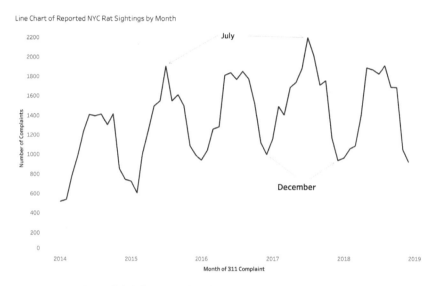

Figure 5.19. Calls to complain about rat sightings in NYC over time.

As we can see, the number of calls to complain about rats rises in the summer months and falls in the winter months. If we assumed that next month's calls would be about the same as this month's calls, we'd underestimate the amount for about half of the year and overestimate the amount for the other half. There's a pattern of rising and falling that we can use to make more educated guesses about future call volumes.

Why are there more calls to complain about rats in the summer months than in the winter? We can make a number of guesses related to rats and how they take shelter during the cold New York winters, but ultimately those are just guesses.

Going back to our example of the relationship between rat sightings in New York City and building permits in Seattle, seasonality is likely the common thread between these two variables. Obviously neither phenomenon is directly causing the other. Instead, they are both rising and falling with the temperature, as shown in Figure 5.20:

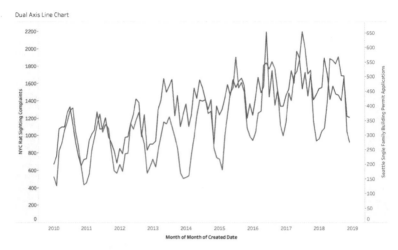

Figure 5.20. The hidden connection between rat sightings and building permit applications.

Forecasting the Future

Once we identify a pattern and find a suitable model for that pattern, we can take the obvious next step and project that pattern into the future. This is known as a forecast. If we are running the call center that takes complaints, or if we are the planner for an animal control service, we could use the historical rat sighting data to get a sense for how many rat sightings we might expect to see in future months:

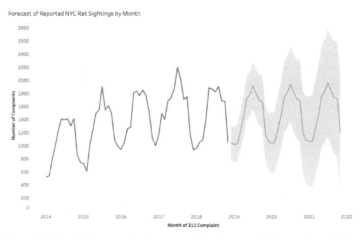

Figure 5.21. A simple forecast of calls to complain about rat sightings in New York City.

We can see that the model attempts to account for the seasonal pattern observed in the historical data. And we can also notice that the uncertainty in the model increases the farther we project the pattern into the future, as indicated by the width of the shaded region around the forecasted line.

The goal in this section isn't to explain how to create the model, or to investigate the algorithms in detail, but rather to understand the concept of forecasting and how it's used.

One very important point about predictive analytics is that simple forecasts assume that historical patterns will continue into the future. But we all know that things can change. The future doesn't always conform obediently to our models created with historical data.

Consider, for example, the number of people filing unemployment claims in the United States. In mid-March 2020, as states across the country issued "stay-at-home" orders in response to the COVID-19 pandemic, entire professions found themselves unable to support themselves. This was an unprecedented scenario in modern times, and we can be sure that no forecast of the unemployment claims figure came anywhere close to predicting the behavior seen in Figure 5.22 below:

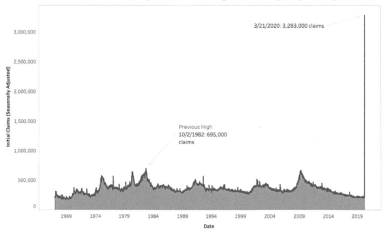

Figure 5.22. Initial weekly unemployment claims area chart in the United States.

This is why forecasts need to come with an asterisk or a warning. Forecasts are often very close to being right. But sometimes they turn out to be wildly off.

5. Prescriptive

Prescriptive Data Analysis is the final type of data analysis we'll cover in this chapter, and it builds on the previous four types of analysis. Prescriptive analytics focuses our attention on various courses of action we could take as well as their likely outcomes.

This approach enables us to make an informed guess about which we think will be the best alternative, allowing us to turn decisions into data-informed decisions.

Prescriptive Data Analysis seeks to answer the question:

What Should We Do?

In order to answer this important question, we must remember that prescriptive analytics involves models built with assumptions about known parameters. These parameters have elements of variation and uncertainty to them, and there are also parameters that remain unknown. So there's always a degree of uncertainty in what our models predict.

We might use this approach to capitalize on an opportunity, and we might use it to mitigate a risk. A common example is deciding which products to cross-sell or up-sell to a customer in the checkout line (virtual or physical) based on what other customers have purchased or rated in the past. This is known as affinity analysis or market basket analysis. Online retailers typically create recommendation engines that leverage and automate this technique.

Prescriptive analysis doesn't necessarily have to be automated, though. Decisions can also involve a "human-in-the-loop", scenarios in which the model or models employed require human interaction. Think of a time when you played online chess and the software made recommendations for your next move, including a likelihood of ultimately winning associated with each move. In that mode, the decision about where to move your piece is still yours to make.

Wrapping It Up

In summary, the five types of data analysis can be compared to a patient visiting the doctor's office. The doctor starts by observing and measuring the patient's symptoms. That's like descriptive analysis. They might need to make some inferences to other patients or studies. That's like inferential analysis. They might probe a little further in an attempt to diagnose the underlying cause of the symptoms. That's like diagnostic analysis. They then make some predictions about how the disease is going to play out over time without intervention. That's like predictive analysis. And finally, they prescribe medication or a procedure to improve the patient's chance of recovery. That's like prescriptive analysis.

This process doesn't start and stop a single time; it often iterates, and we take what we learn and start over, a little wiser the next time. Often the outcome of our analysis isn't an answer to a question, but rather a new question to ask, one that we didn't anticipate in the beginning, and that requires us to gather new data or information in order to answer. That's okay, too. We don't always know what is happening at the root level of our observations, and once we set in motion a data-informed decision, we will have a brand new set of circumstances to analyze.

Chapter 6

THE SIX WAYS OF DISPLAYING DATA

"There is quite a difference between simply looking at a chart and seeing it."

– Mary Eleanor Spear

As human beings, we take in information about our environment using five different senses: the faculties of sight, smell, hearing, taste, and touch. When we interact with data in digital form, it's possible for us to use each of these different senses as well. We can see data, hear it, feel it, and even taste it and smell it if it's converted into the right form.

Research into data sonification—the use of non-speech audio to convey information—has been expanding in recent decades[49] and tools such as Two Tone are becoming available to create sound and even music out of data.[50] Data physicalization involves turning data into physical objects that humans can touch and even potentially smell and taste.

But we primarily use sight and hearing to interact with the data contained in the spreadsheets and databases that have become ubiquitous in our world. We'll focus on these two senses in this chapter on how we take in data and process it. Each of the six ways of displaying data that we'll consider has a valid use, and none should be considered inherently

---

49. https://www.wired.com/2007/04/data-sonification/
50. https://twotone.io/

bad or inferior. They're just good at enabling us to perform different cognitive tasks.

The visual system is a magnificent element of the central nervous system. Light waves bounce off of objects around us and enter our eyes through the cornea and lens, which refract the light and shine it onto the back of the retina. The rods and cones of the retina turn this image into electrical pulses, which are carried by the optical nerve through the lateral geniculate nucleus (LGN) in the thalamus and into the visual cortex of the brain, which is located in the back of our skull in the occipital lobe.

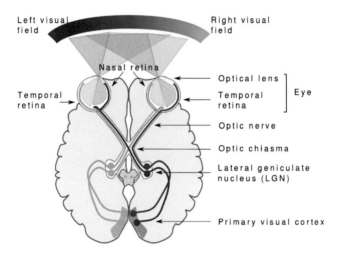

Figure 6.1. The human visual pathway.[51]

In this relatively recently evolved area of our brain, we use these signals to recognize patterns and to process information about objects in motion and at objects at rest. This includes objects that we will consider in this chapter.

Let's start with the simplest form of display: a single data point shown as a number.

---

51. https://commons.wikimedia.org/wiki/File:Human_visual_pathway.svg

1. Figures

One of the key aspects of data literacy is *numeracy*, which is the ability to understand and work with numbers.[52] A basic part of this ability is understanding what numbers themselves mean, and correctly interpreting them when we see them all around us in daily life.

Many times all we encounter or all we're looking for is a single data point—one solitary figure without context or history. While this type of data can be very limited, there's nothing inherently wrong with the act of considering a single number. There are scenarios in which a full spreadsheet or a fancy display would be overkill. In fact, as we'll see later on in the chapter, it can be an effective practice to show the most important metrics in prominent places of more complex displays.

Let's say you're working at a sandwich shop and you're responsible for making sandwiches for orders as they come in. At any given point in time, you need to know how many sandwiches to make to fulfill the current order. If you asked your coworker who takes orders from the customer how many veggie sandwiches you need to make for the business meeting down the street, and they gave you a multifaceted display of historical orders complete with predictive analytics about future trends, you'd look at them a little funny, wouldn't you?

Operational scenarios (*How many sandwiches do I need to make right now?*) or simple curiosity (*How many people lived in Sweden in 2017?*) often require nothing less and nothing more than a single number. How that number is displayed is another matter. There are different numeral systems that help us capture and convey quantities.

The simplest form of communicating quantities are tally marks, also known as the **unary numeral system**. In this system, if you wish to represent a certain number, then you just repeat some symbol that many times. It can be any symbol, but the one you're likely most familiar with is the vertical tick lines used in tally marks, with every fifth line crossing through the previous four at an angle:

Figure 6.2. The common form of tally marks.[53]

52. https://www.merriam-webster.com/dictionary/numeracy
53. https://commons.wikimedia.org/wiki/File:Tally_marks.svg

This system of displaying quantitative information is ancient. The Czechoslovakian wolf bone, which dates back to 30,000 years ago, was found in 1937 in Moravia and it bears 57 tick marks that appear to have been made deliberately. Pliny the Elder, who lived from AD 23 to 79, wrote about which type of wood was the best for keeping tallies. From counting sheep in the pasture to days in jail, humans have been using simple tally marks like these to keep track of quantities for millennia.

If we double the number of symbols used to express numbers from one to two, we move from the unary numeral system to the **binary numeral system**, also called the base-2 numeral system. While people don't typically use binary to read data or to communicate it to each other, this system is the primary numeral system used by all modern computers due to the ease of implementation with logic gates like transistors that act as switches between two alternative "on" or "off" states, called Booleans.

The following figure shows zero along with the first seven numbers of the binary numeral system, and how these numerical displays would be converted into decimal numbers. The right-most digit in the 3-digit binary sequence represents 2^0 or 1, the second digit from the right represents 2^1, or 2, and the third digit from the right represents 2^2, or 4. If we were to add a fourth digit to the left, it would represent a value 2^3, or 8, and so on.

Binary Number				Decimal Number		
0	0	0	=	$0 + 0 + 0$	= 0
0	0	1	=	$0 + 0 + 2^0$	= 1
0	1	0	=	$0 + 2^1 + 0$	= 2
0	1	1	=	$0 + 2^1 + 2^0$	= 3
1	0	0	=	$2^2 + 0 + 0$	= 4
1	0	1	=	$2^2 + 0 + 2^0$	= 5
1	1	0	=	$2^2 + 2^1 + 0$	= 6
1	1	1	=	$2^2 + 2^1 + 2^0$	= 7

Figure. 6.3. The binary numeral system and conversion to decimal.

A far more common system that we humans use to both read and communicate quantities is the **decimal numeral system**. Decimal comes from the Latin word *decima,* which means to tithe, or pay a tenth part of something. In the etymology of the word, we can see the connection to the number ten.

This ubiquitous numeral system was invented by mathematicians in India between the first and fourth centuries AD and adopted by Arabic mathematicians like Al-Kindi in the ninth century AD. For this reason, the decimal numeral system is often called the **Hindu-Arabic numeral system.**[54] It later spread to Europe during the High Middle Ages, and a version of this numeral system is currently the dominant system used in the West.

According to this popular system, the number of unique symbols used to keep track of quantities increases from the two different symbols of binary to ten different symbols. Of course we know these as the numbers 0, 1, 2, 3, 4, 5, 6, 7, 8, and 9.

Within the decimal numeral system, there are different types of numbers. A whole number is a number without any fractions (or an "integer" if it can be negative). If we take a whole number like 10,057,698, which happens to be the population of Sweden in 2017, we see that there are 8 different digits in the number. The first digit on the right, 8, is in the ones place ($10^0 = 1$), representing 8 individuals. The next digit to the left, 9, is in the tens place ($10^1 = 10$), representing nine groups of ten individuals. The next digit to the left, 6, is in the hundreds place ($10^2 = 100$), representing six groups of 100 individuals. And so on.

Notice that in the population figure above, we used a comma to indicate the thousands separator. The first number after the first comma on the right, 7, is in the thousands place.

The United States and the UK commonly use a comma for the thousands separator, but many countries around the world use a period, like this:

$$10.057.698$$

Other countries, including Sweden, use a thin space, like this:

$$10\,057\,698$$

---

54. https://en.wikipedia.org/wiki/Hindu%E2%80%93Arabic_numeral_system

Others, like China, use a ten thousands separator instead of a thousands separator, yielding 1005,7689. And of course numbers can be shown without any separator at all: 10057689.

There are also differences between what symbol is used as the decimal place to display fractions of a unit. Some use a period for the decimal place, displaying "2.5" to indicate two and a half, while others use a comma to express the exact same value: "2,5." Older versions or hand-written figures in some places use a dot: 2·5, or an apostrophe: 2'5.

So we see that even simply displaying data as a solitary figure can be confusing. To avoid misinterpreting the true value, care must be taken to ensure we know what numeral system is being used, and what conventions are being used for separators.

2. Tables

Sometimes a single number isn't sufficient. We need to see the numbers broken out by category, or we need to see numbers side by side with other numbers for comparison purposes. In cases like these, a table can be a useful way of displaying data.

A table of numbers is defined as "a systematic arrangement of data usually in rows and columns for ready reference."[55] Humans have been using such grids of numbers for centuries. One example of an ancient table is Plimpton 322, a clay multiplication table believed to have been created during the Old Babylonian period at around 1,800 BCE.[56] It's currently housed at Columbia University, and it contains four columns and 15 rows of mathematical figures, specifically showing two of the three figures in "Pythagorean triples," numbers that follow the relationship $a^2 + b^2 = c^2$:

Figure 64. Plimpton 322, a clay tablet containing lists of Pythagorean triples.

55. https://www.merriam-webster.com/dictionary/table
56. https://en.wikipedia.org/wiki/Plimpton_322

Fast forward a couple thousand years and we find yet another table, this one part of the 1800 U.S. Census showing population by county and demographic variables. The column headers "Free White Males" and "Slaves" offer a stark but important reminder about what the information on the tables we create tells the world and those to come about us.

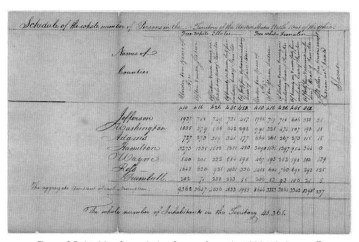

Figure 6.5. A table of population figures from the 1800 U.S. Census.[57]

It's easy to see why tables and computers would make a natural pair. The marriage took place in 1963 in the early days of the Third Industrial Revolution with BCL, which stood for Business Computer Language. BCL was written in the programming language FORTRAN and it was implemented on the IBM 1130, a computer that made use of punched cards.

Awareness about the spreadsheet as a tool skyrocketed in 1979, as a program called VisiCalc was implemented on the Apple II, the first computer sold by Apple Computer, Inc. The program was adapted for the IBM PC in 1981. This software application has been credited with turning the personal computer from a toy primarily used by hobbyists into a serious tool for businesses to use for accounting and other necessary functions.

57. https://www2.census.gov/library/photos/1800-a.jpg

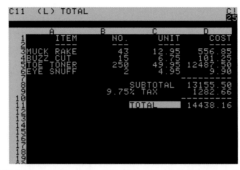

Figure 6.6. VisiCalc, the first spreadsheet created for the personal computer.[58]

There are many spreadsheet software products available today, such as Microsoft Excel and Apple's Numbers, and the spreadsheet has moved online with applications like Google Sheets and Zoho. These applications allow users to enter or upload data into cells arranged in the same rows and columns used so long ago in Babylon. Users can enter formulas to perform a wide array of calculations on the data contained in these cells, making spreadsheets a common and invaluable data working tool in today's professional environment.

Another critical computer application that makes extensive use of tables is the **database**. At around the same time that spreadsheets were making their debut on the personal computer, **relational databases** were becoming the dominant way to collect, store, and access data. A relational database has the potential to hold massive amounts of data housed in various tables that are linked together by common fields.

Instead of "rows," a database has "tuples," sometimes called "records." And instead of "columns," a database has "attributes" or "fields."

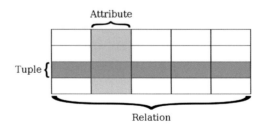

Figure 6.7. Relational database terms.[59]

58. https://en.wikipedia.org/wiki/VisiCalc
59. https://en.wikipedia.org/wiki/Relation_(database)

THE SIX WAYS OF DISPLAYING DATA

Data engineers construct these and other more modern forms of unstructured databases. Data analysts query them for needed records using SQL, or Structured Query Language. More on these activities and others in the next chapter.

So just what are tables good for, then? Among other things, they allow us to capture measurements and records and store them, and they allow us to access these measurements and records at a later date to perform analysis.

To illustrate the comparative value of tables, statistics, and data visualizations, let's consider four different sets of pairs of numbers known as Anscombe's Quartet. The founding chairperson of Yale's statistics department, Francis Anscombe, came up with the interesting quartet in 1973.

I		II		III		IV	
x	y	x	y	x	y	x	y
10	8.04	10	9.14	10	7.46	8	6.58
8	6.95	8	8.14	8	6.77	8	5.76
13	7.58	13	8.74	13	12.74	8	7.71
9	8.81	9	8.77	9	7.11	8	8.84
11	8.33	11	9.26	11	7.81	8	8.47
14	9.96	14	8.1	14	8.84	8	7.04
6	7.24	6	6.13	6	6.08	8	5.25
4	4.26	4	3.1	4	5.39	19	12.5
12	10.84	12	9.13	12	8.15	8	5.56
7	4.82	7	7.26	7	6.42	8	7.91
5	5.68	5	4.74	5	5.73	8	6.89

Figure 6.8. Anscombe's Quartet.[60]

If you take a look at these eight columns, you'll notice that they're broken up into four main sections, labeled by roman numerals (I, II, III and IV), and that each of these sections sections has two columns, one labeled "x" and the other labeled "y." Each x and y column has eleven rows of numbers. Beyond that, it's difficult to make much of these figures just by looking at them.

Let's consider whether summary statistics can give us any additional information about this mysterious quartet. What do these numbers mean, and what do we learn from them?

---

60. https://en.wikipedia.org/wiki/Anscombe%27s_quartet

3. Statistics

In the section on Descriptive Data Analysis, we considered a number of summary statistics, such as measures of central tendency (mean, median, and mode) and measures of dispersion (variance, standard deviation). Of course this only scratches the surface of the full field of descriptive statistics, and we don't intend to replicate entire textbooks here.

As we learned in that section, summary statistics are incredibly useful for distilling a set of numbers down to a relatively small set of representative numbers. This can help us get a sense of what a typical value might look like, and how much the individual values might vary from a particular center point.

What's interesting about Anscombe's Quartet is that the summary statistics of each of these four sections of values are incredibly similar. The averages and variances are identical or nearly identical, the correlation between x and y is the same, and so is the equation of the best-fit line:

	I		II		III		IV	
	x	y	x	y	x	y	x	y
	10	8.04	10	9.14	10	7.46	8	6.58
	8	6.95	8	8.14	8	6.77	8	5.76
	13	7.58	13	8.74	13	12.74	8	7.71
	9	8.81	9	8.77	9	7.11	8	8.84
	11	8.33	11	9.26	11	7.81	8	8.47
	14	9.96	14	8.1	14	8.84	8	7.04
	6	7.24	6	6.13	6	6.08	8	5.25
	4	4.26	4	3.1	4	5.39	19	12.5
	12	10.84	12	9.13	12	8.15	8	5.56
	7	4.82	7	7.26	7	6.42	8	7.91
	5	5.68	5	4.74	5	5.73	8	6.89
Mean	9	7.50	9	7.50	9	7.50	9	7.50
Variance	11.000	4.127	11.000	4.128	11.000	4.123	11.000	4.123
Standard Deviation	3.32	2.03	3.32	2.03	3.32	2.03	3.32	2.03
Correlation between x and y	0.816		0.816		0.816		0.817	
Linear regression line	y = 3.00 + 0.500x		y = 3.00 + 0.500x		y = 3.00 + 0.500x		y = 3.00 + 0.500x	
Coefficient of determination, R^2	0.67		0.67		0.67		0.67	

Figure 6.9. Anscombe's Quartet with summary statistics rows added at the bottom.

If that were the end of the story, then Anscombe's Quartet would simply show that it's possible to create different sets of numbers that have very similar statistical properties. That wouldn't be anything new, and we wouldn't be considering the quartet right now if that's all that we could learn from it.

The real value of the quartet is what we learn about the columns of numbers when we plot them on a Cartesian coordinate system. In the previous chapter, we considered this important convention of plotting pairs of numbers on a two dimensional plan with a horizontal axis (x) and a vertical one (y). Let's do that with Anscombe's Quartet.

4. Visualizations

When we visualize data, we use different types of **encodings** to turn quantitative and categorical data values into graphical attributes that combine together to form the charts and graphs we see everyday.

For example, if we use the values in the x column to place dots horizontally, and the values in the y columns to place them vertically, then we get the following four scatter plots for each of the four sets in the quartet:

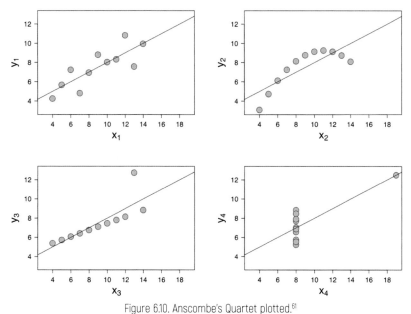

Figure 6.10. Anscombe's Quartet plotted.[61]

What's remarkable about Anscombe's Quartet is that when we graph the four sets, we immediately spot patterns that were totally invisible

---

61. By Anscombe.svg: Schutz(label using subscripts): Avenue - Anscombe.svg, CC BY-SA 3.0, https://commons.wikimedia.org/w/index.php?curid=9838454

in both the tables and the summary statistics. We see a noisy line (I, top left), a parabola or arc (II, top right), a slanted line with an outlier (III, bottom left), and a vertical line with an extreme outlier (IV, bottom right). We simply can't see these relationships at all in the tables, nor can we see the patterns in the summary statistics.

Some use Anscombe's Quartet to try to make the point that visualizing data is the *only* useful way to display it, but this isn't what the example shows us. Each of the three forms of displaying data has its own unique value:

- The tables show each of the values with a high degree of **precision.**
- The statistics give a sense of central **tendency** and dispersion.
- The visualizations reveal the **patterns** inherent in the data.

Visualizing data in the form of charts and graphs isn't as old as tally marks or tables, but it's certainly not new. Some of the earliest forms of visualization of empirical data (as opposed to abstract figures from mathematical equations) were published over 250 years ago. Let's consider some of the more well-known visualizations created by the pioneers of yesterday.

In 1765, **Joseph Priestley** published "A Chart of Biography" to give his students a perspective on the course of human history. The chart shows the start and end of the lives of famous people in history as horizontal lines going from left (birth) to right (death). In all, his chart spans 1200 BCE to AD 1800 and includes two thousand historical figures like Aristotle, Euclid, and Cyrus, among many others.

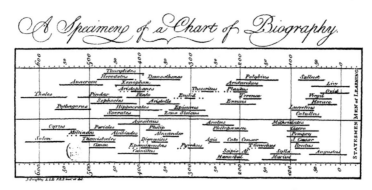

Figure 6.11. Joseph Priestley's "A Chart of Biography."[62]

62. https://en.wikipedia.org/wiki/A_Chart_of_Biography#/media/File:PriestleyChart.gif

William Playfair, a Scottish engineer who lived from 1759 to 1823, is often thought of as the founder of graphical methods of statistics. He is credited with inventing a number of chart types that are in common use today, including the line chart, the area chart, and the bar chart.

In 1786, two decades after Priestley published "A Chart of Biography" Playfair published his famous work "The Commercial and Political Atlas" in which he included a set of 34 stained copper plate charts showing the balance of trade between England and various other nations. The figure below shows one of the 34 plates, the exports and imports to and from Denmark and Norway from 1700 to 1780. Note how Playfair explains to his readers how to interpret the charts in the caption at the bottom: "The Bottom line is divided into Years, the Right hand line into £10,000 each."

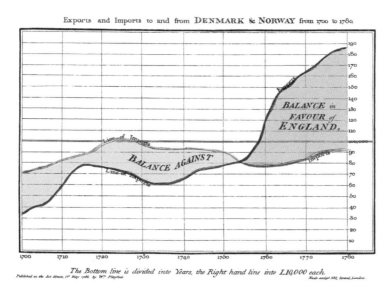

Figure 6.12. One of the 34 plates of William Playfair's 1786 work "Commercial and Political Atlas."[63]

It's worth quoting Playfair at length out of his later work *The Statistical Breviary* (London, 1801), in which the first known pie chart was published, to understand his perspective on the value of visualizing data:

63. https://en.wikipedia.org/wiki/William_Playfair#/media/File:Playfair_TimeSeries-2.png

The advantages proposed by this mode of representation (his charts), are to facilitate the attainment of information, and aid the memory in retaining it: which two points form the principal business in what we call learning, or the acquisition of knowledge.

Of all the senses, the eye gives the liveliest and most accurate idea of whatever is susceptible of being represented to it; and when proportion between different quantities is the object, then the eye has an incalculable superiority; as from the constant, and even involuntary habit of comparing the sizes of objects it has acquired the capacity of doing so, with an accuracy that is almost unequalled. (p. 14)

And so we see that encoding quantitative values using visual channels or marks such as length, angle, area, and color enables us to move up the DIKW pyramid from "Information" to "Knowledge" by making fast visual associations.

He mentions one other value of visualization later in the introduction to *The Statistical Breviary*: enlivening the learning process for students of statistics:

It is presumed that to students this work will be particularly useful: for no study is less alluring or more dry and tedious than statistics, unless the mind and imagination are set to work, or that the person studying is particularly interested in the subject; which last can seldom be the case with young men in any rank of life. (p. 16)

There are many other talented pioneers of the field of data visualization that we could discuss at length, but any discussion about such pioneers that left out **Florence Nightingale** would be woefully inadequate. Nightingale, who was born in 1820 and died in 1910, is known as the founder of modern nursing, but she also made an indelible mark on the field of data visualization along the way.

She was not only a devoted and influential nurse, known affectionately as the "Lady with the Lamp" for the rounds she made checking on soldiers, but she was also a talented statistician. Her 1858 work *Notes on*

Matters Affecting the Health, Efficiency, and Hospital Administration of the British Army[64] documented the causes of death of British soldiers in the squalid field hospitals in Turkey during the Crimean War. She included in this work influential diagrams that illustrated the reality of life for soldiers in the army.

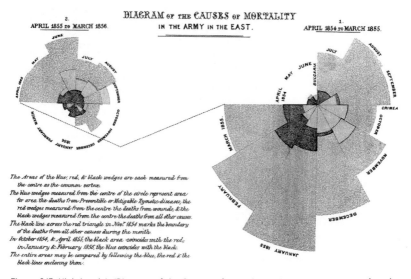

Figure 6.13. Nightingale's "Diagram of the Causes of Mortality in the Army in the East" (1858).

These creative polar area diagrams that she called "coxcombs" made it painfully clear that soldiers were primarily dying of communicable diseases (the area of the grayish blue wedges) as opposed to wounds suffered in battle (the area of the red wedges). They also show the increase in death rate in the winter months, each wedge representing a month of the year, as soldiers were huddled in field hospitals with little to no sanitation.

The most noteworthy fact about these infographics is that they prompted sweeping policy changes and ultimately saved lives. Nightingale presented them to Queen Victoria, leading to sanitation reform in the field hospitals and a dramatic reduction in death rates, as seen in the diagram on the left hand side.

---

64. https://wellcomecollection.org/works/sz9sms2m/items?canvas=1

These pioneers and many others laid the groundwork for the representation of data using encodings like length, area, and color in charts and graphs. They created the first expressions of the visual language of data that have evolved since their day. Their creations were innovations, and their audiences needed to be taught how to read them.

If we fast-forward to our day, we live at a time when charts and graphs are ubiquitous. Research into the relative effectiveness of different encoding types has provided us with a better understanding of the way our brains interpret charts and graphs. Many questions remain unanswered, but we now know, for example, that we're better at guessing the true proportions in the data if the numbers are encoded as length (such as in a bar chart) versus area (such as in a packed bubble chart) or angle (such as in a pie chart).

To bring this concept to life, look at the charts below and hazard a guess about the value for the red marks (bars, slices, and circles) if the value of the blue marks is 1.0 in each of them:

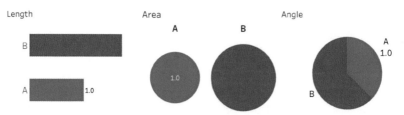

Figure 6.14. Estimating proportions when different encoding types are used.

The answer is that in each case, the red mark has a value of 1.7. The length of the red bar is 1.7, the area of the red circle is 1.7, and the angle of the red portion of the circle (or "pie") is 1.7. But you can see how it's much easier to come up with a guess that's close to 1.7 using the bars on the left.

This is a very simplistic way of explaining the basic idea behind some of the data visualization experiments that have taken place in the past few decades. Those experiments have led us to a place where we feel that some encodings are easier for humans to accurately decode than others.

Dr. Tamara Munzner, professor of computer science at the University of British Columbia in Vancouver and an expert in information visualization, has created a very helpful graphic that explains the current thinking around the order of effectiveness of encodings. Channels, or encodings, that are higher up on the list are more "effective" in this sense. Note that "Length (1D size)" is higher up on the list of channels than both "Tilt/angle" and "Area (2D size)." This jives with our simple experiment testing the size of marks using Figure 6.14 above.

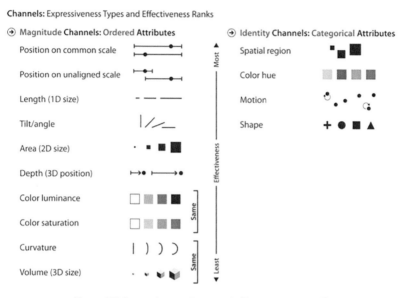

Figure 6.15. Expressiveness Types and Effectiveness Ranks.[65]

As we've seen, data visualizations are an incredibly useful tool to help us find patterns and estimate proportions that are otherwise hidden in tables of data. This is true even for individual charts and graphs such as the ones created by the pioneers discussed above. Sometimes, however, showing multiple data visualizations together in a single view can help us uncover even more in our data.

65. Tamara Munzner, *Visualization Analysis and Design,* with illustrations by Eamonn Maguire (A K Peters Visualization Series, CRC Press, 2014).

5. Dashboards

What's a dashboard, and where does the term come from?

Prior to the invention of the automobile, a "dashboard" was a piece of wood or leather that separated the riders from the horse of a carriage and blocked the mud that was "dashed up" by the horses hooves, preventing it from hitting the riders in the face.

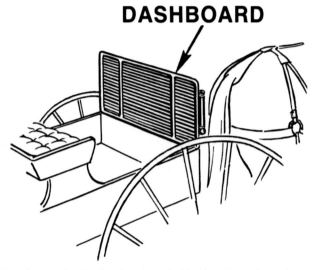

Figure 6.16. A diagram showing the placement of a "dashboard" on a horse-drawn carriage.[66]

When the first automobiles started showing up around the turn of the twentieth century, the dashboard was retained in order to block mud from the turning wheels, and also to block heat and oil from the engine.

Gradually, as the design of the automobile evolved, the dashboard was a convenient place to house gauges and instrumentation of various types to allow the driver to be aware of how the car was operating at any given time. Modern automobile dashboards (sometimes called dash, instrument panel, or fascia) are sophisticated displays of information that typically include gauges, individual data points, and indicators of various sorts.

---

66. https://en.wikipedia.org/wiki/Dashboard#/media/File:Dashboard_(PSF).png

Figure 6.17. A modern automobile dashboard.[67]

Today, we also use the term "data dashboard" to describe views of data that combine elements such as figures, statistics, tables, and data visualizations in order to communicate multiple aspects of a situation so that those using it can be informed about the current state of affairs.

In this way a data dashboard is similar to an automobile dashboard. A driver can look at the car's dashboard to see her speed, how far she has traveled, how much fuel is left, and so on. And a business owner or process manager can look at the data dashboard to see critical metrics, often termed KPIs (key process indicators) in order to know how well the process is running.

In their book *Big Book of Dashboards,* authors Steve Wexler, Andy Cotgreave, and Jeff Shaffer settled on this concise definition:

> *A dashboard is a visual display of data used to monitor conditions and/ or facilitate understanding.*[68]

Let's consider a data dashboard that shows the population of the world by region and country, and how it has changed over time. If you'd like to interact with the dashboard yourself, you can go to https://bit.ly/ worldpopdash.

67. Photo by Mike from Pexels: https://www.pexels.com/photo/black-car-instrument-cluster-panel-945443/
68. https://www.bigbookofdashboards.com/

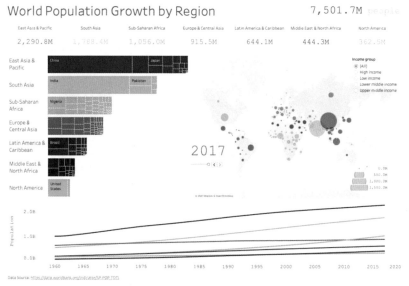

Figure 6.18. World Population Dashboard.

This dashboard includes the following ways of displaying data:

- A large **figure** at the top (sometimes referred to as "BAN," an acronym that stands for "Big Ass Number") showing the total population
- Another **figure** in the center showing the year along with a slider control to change the year
- A **table** across the top showing the population by region
- A **visualization** (treemap) on the left showing the population by country and broken out by regions
- A **visualization** (map) on the right showing population by country
- A **visualization** (line chart) at the bottom showing the change in regional population over time

This is what is often referred to as an "exploratory dashboard," as opposed to an "explanatory dashboard," since the primary purpose is to allow a user to investigate a topic and to ask and get answers for a whole host of questions.

In order to enable the user to explore the data, a dashboard includes different interactive elements:

Tooltips

Dashboards often allow the users to hover over an object to get more information about that data point. For example, if we hover over the box in the treemap for Nigeria, then a popup window called a "tooltip" appears telling the user the country, region, and population in 2017:

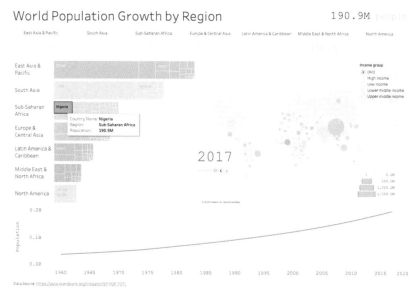

Figure 6.19. The World Population Dashboard with a tooltip hovering over the treemap.

Highlighting

If you look closely at the version of the dashboard in the figure above, you'll notice that a few other changes have also occurred beyond the tooltip appearing. First, the rectangle for Nigeria in the treemap is the full original color (orange), but all the other rectangles in the treemap have been washed out. Similarly, the circle in the map on the right for Nigeria remains its full color (orange), but the other circles have all been washed out slightly, too. This is what is called "Highlighting." Our interrogation of the rectangle for Nigeria has resulted in Highlights that shine the spotlight on this data point.

Filtering

You'll also notice if you look closely that the line chart has changed to show only the population line for Nigeria, and the total population BAN (figure at the top right) is now showing just Nigeria's population in 2017. This is called filtering.

If you'd like to focus on specific elements in the data, then it can help if the dashboard allows you to remove, or filter out, other elements. For example, let's say you were only interested in population growth in the Sub-Saharan Africa region. The thin table across the top has been set up to act as a filter, meaning if you click on the value for Sub-Saharan Africa, then the entire dashboard will change to show only that region:

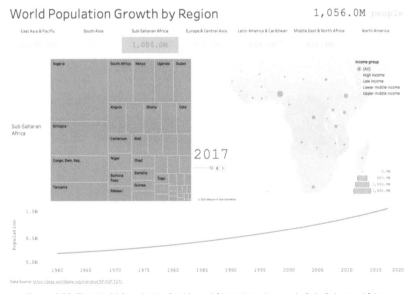

Figure 6.20. The World Population Dashboard filtered to show only Sub-Saharan Africa.

Additionally, if you look in the top right corner of the map, you will notice that there is a "radio button" selector that allows you to filter based on country income group classification. Currently, this filter is set to "All," meaning that it is showing all countries of the world regardless of their income group classification. If we change this to select "Lower middle income," then we'll change the dashboard to show only those countries that currently belong to that group. We can see that countries in this grouping accounted for almost 3 million people around the world in 2017, that South Asia was the region with the largest population of lower-middle-income countries, and that India was by far the largest lower-middle-income country in terms of population in 2017:

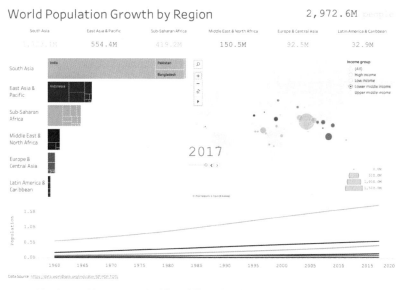

Figure 6.21. The World Population Dashboard filtered to show lower-middle-income countries.

Thanks to the ability to bring in multiple views and make them interactive, exploratory dashboards can be very powerful and efficient ways for people to learn about a data set. The user can go down many different paths of inquiry to learn about the topic based on their own curiosity and interest.

Sometimes, though, we want to walk an audience through a specific set of findings that help them develop a specific understanding. At times like these, an exploratory dashboard may not be the best display. After all, how can we be sure that they will explore the right aspects of the dashboard, and in the right order?

In cases like this, we turn to data storytelling.

6. Data Stories

The term "data storytelling" has been increasing in usage over the past decade, but what, exactly is a data story? Some understand the term to refer simply to a finding or insight gleaned from data, while others understand it to be more involved than that.

In their seminal 2010 paper on the topic titled "Narrative Visualization: Telling Stories With Data," Jeffrey Heer and Edward Segel describe "an emerging class of visualizations" that attempt to "combine narratives with interactive graphics." They call them "tours through visualized data."[69]

According to this way of using the term, a data story is much more than a single factoid or chart. We can attempt to define the term as follows:

> *A data story is a set of **findings** gleaned from data and brought together into a **sequence** that forms a **cohesive narrative** and that provides an audience with a deeper understanding of a topic.*

There are a few key elements to this definition. A first key element of this definition is the word "findings". Each part of the data story—each story point—consists of one or more data findings. These findings can be communicated by a data storyteller via simple numbers or statements including numbers ("The population of the United States increased by 35% from 1985 to 2015."), or they can be communicated via data visualizations: charts, graphs, maps and dashboards.

The second key element is the word "sequence." A data story according to this definition has more than one part to it, and the various parts are connected together in a particular order. Typically, a data story can be said to have a beginning and an end, and it can often contain one or more middle sections as well.

A third key element of the definition is the phrase "cohesive narrative." The Oxford dictionary defines "narrative" as "a spoken or written

---

69. http://vis.stanford.edu/files/2010-Narrative-InfoVis.pdf

account of connected events; a story." And the word "cohesive" is a form of the word "cohesion," which means "the action or fact of forming a united whole." The figures and visuals strung together in a specific order in a data story are accompanied by words. These words take the form of spoken words verbalized in a presentation or a recording, or written words included in the view as annotations, headlines, or captions. Often both verbal and written narratives accompany a data story.

This is the meaning of the term "data story" as we will use it in this section. That doesn't mean it's the only possible way to use the term. But it is a fitting term for a form of communication that's becoming more and more important, both in the companies in which we work and in the communities in which we live.

Let's consider an example from the global population data set that we have been using in this chapter.

We can start off by showing that the population of the world has grown in a straight line since 1960, rising from just over 3 billion to more than 7.5 billion people over that time. This line chart is accompanied by the annotation: "The overall population of the world has risen steadily over almost 6 decades."

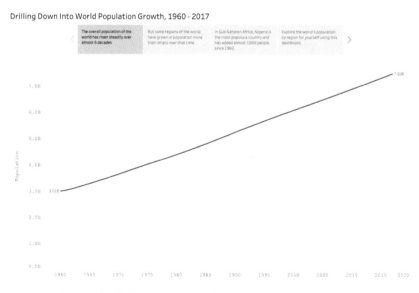

Figure 6.22. The first story point: a global population change line chart.

We can then break it down by region, showing how the different regions of the world have different population sizes, and that these populations have grown at different rates over that same period of time. This second story point in the sequence is also a line chart, this one showing different lines for seven different regions of the world, each with its own unique color. This story point is accompanied by this annotation: "But some regions of the world have grown in population more than others over that time."

Drilling Down Into World Population Growth, 1960 - 2017

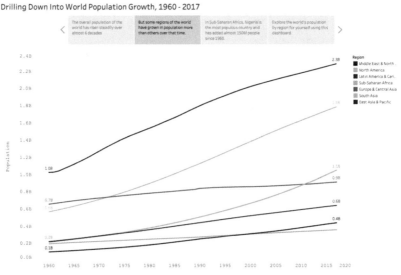

Figure 6.23. A second story point with population broken out by region.

This transition from the total population of the world to the population of each region is effectively "drilling down," as we discussed in the previous chapter when we considered diagnostic data analysis.

We can drill down further into one of the regions that seems to suggest further analysis: Sub-Saharan Africa, whose growth has an uprising curve to it. If we create a third story point showing line charts for each country in the region of Sub-Saharan Africa, we can talk about the increase in population of countries like Nigeria and Ethiopia. This third story point is accompanied by this annotation: "In Sub-Saharan Africa, Nigeria is the most populous country and has added almost 150M people since 1960."

Drilling Down Into World Population Growth, 1960 - 2017

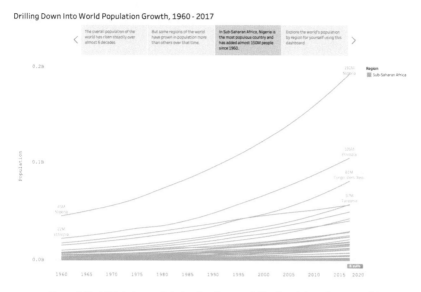

Figure 6.24. A third story point showing the population breakdown in one region

This is a simple example of a data story that we can use to take an audience down a path of enlightenment that is difficult if not impossible to replicate with a single figure, table, visualization, or dashboard. Sometimes these data stories are told via slides as live presentations in a real or virtual conference room, and other times they are told as "long-form" articles, reports, or blog posts, and other times they are recorded and uploaded to the internet as videos.

In summary, each of these six ways of displaying data have their own uses, and they can be combined to great effect as we work with others to move up the DIKW pyramid discussed at the beginning of the book.

Chapter 7

THE SEVEN GROUPS OF DATA ACTIVITIES

"Alone we can do so little; together we can do so much."

– Helen Keller

When teams of people work together to turn data into wisdom, they need to perform different tasks or activities throughout the process. These tasks aren't necessarily dedicated to any one job or role, and they don't necessarily happen in order in a linear fashion. In large organizations, each of the different activities are taking place continually, and they feed into each other in various ways.

Let's consider each of these activities one by one to get a better understanding of how teams can work together more effectively. In so doing we can gain a deeper appreciation for our own contributions to a data-informed culture.

The seven groups of data activities are creating data, building data sources, curating data, analyzing data, presenting data, consuming data, and making data-informed decisions:

Figure 7.1. The seven activities of a data team.

1. Creating Data

Each of us creates data throughout the day, sometimes intentionally and knowingly, and other times unintentionally and unknowingly. When you go for a walk in your neighborhood, whether you turn on a fitness app or not, the phone in your pocket generates location data that is stored on a server somewhere. In this sense, we are all already participants in the Fourth Industrial Revolution that's underway, whether we know it or not.

Let's consider just a small handful of the ways that people in companies intentionally create data for the organization to use:

- Managers enter scores for their direct reports into an online form connected to the company's HR record during the performance appraisal process.

- Technical support representatives enter data into a solutions database or call log while troubleshooting issues on the phone with customers.

- Warehouse managers perform inventory checks and update quantities in the ERP (Enterprise Resource Planning) system.

- Sales representatives add notes about leads and opportunities into a CRM (Customer Relationship Management) system.

- Marketing professionals conduct focus groups to gauge customer satisfaction.

- Research and Development engineers conduct tests on prototypes.

We could brainstorm many other ways that people in every single department in a company create data deliberately each day.

There are also many ways that people in organizations create data unintentionally. They may be performing some action to accomplish a specific goal, and in the background their activities are being captured, recorded, and stored for the company to use in various ways. Often people are aware of this data collection and have agreed to it, and other times this is not the case. For example:

- Scanning a badge to unlock a door and enter a building
- Walking by an RFID (radio-frequency identification) reader while wearing an RFID badge
- Traveling with a company-issued mobile phone device
- Sending an email or chat message to a colleague
- Using company Wi-Fi to browse the internet
- Walking down a hallway and being logged via cameras and face-recognition software

The above examples just scratch the surface of the myriad ways that people create data while going about their various activities as employees.

We also create data as customers and users of various products and platforms. We scan barcodes at the self-checkout line of the grocery store, tap a heart icon on a message posted to a social media platform, or simply open an email in our inbox. All of these activities are tracked and stored in a database for someone to analyze.

We also regularly create data as functioning members of society. We cast votes that are counted in elections, drive automobiles whose speed is measured by a police officer by the side of the road, submit tax returns that are received and stored by the appropriate government agencies, complete census questionnaires, fill out forms for drivers licenses, passports, student loans – and the list goes on and on.

Every year that passes, we create more data than we did the year before.

2. Building Data Sources

With all of the data being created, someone has to design and create a system to gather and store it all in a place where it can be accessed for later use. This can be as simple as manually updating a list or spreadsheet, or it can be as sophisticated as setting up a data warehouse in the cloud.

Indeed, you build a data source every time you jot down your weekly grocery list before going to the market, and so does a vast team of data engineers working for a social media platform so that millions and millions of users can seamlessly interact with one another's content. These are opposite extremes on a spectrum, but they share the purpose of capturing data, storing it, and making it accessible.

When building data sources, various questions need to be taken into account. The disciplines of data engineering and database security and privacy are highly sophisticated and rapidly evolving, so we can't come close to covering all of the bases in this context. Nevertheless, here is a simplified list of the kinds of questions that are often involved in these critical activities:

Where will the data be stored?

- In a spreadsheet, a database, or in documents or files?
- Databases are either "**on premises,**" meaning installed and run on servers located at a site owned by the organization that owns the data, or else a database is remotely located and managed by a third party at a **server farm** or in the **cloud.**
- A cloud can be a **public cloud** (owned and operated by a third party provider) or a **private cloud** (resources dedicated to a single organization or business), and it's also possible to design a **hybrid cloud** solution (a combination of the two). These definitions are becoming blurred by innovative ways companies are working together.

In what structure will the data be stored?

- If the data is to be stored in a **relational database**, data engineers design tables that are linked with **primary keys** and **foreign**

keys. For example, a Customer table may have a primary key called "Customer_id" that uniquely identifies each customer, and an Orders table may have a primary key called "Order_id" that uniquely identifies each order. These two tables can be linked together by including "Customer_id" as a foreign key in the orders table, allowing us to track which customer placed each order:

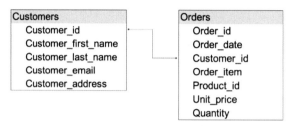

Figure 7.2. A simplified diagram showing two linked tables in a relational database

How often will the data be refreshed?

- Sometimes it's necessary to update a database multiple times per day, even multiple times per minute. And other times a database needs to be updated annually or less.
- An example of a database that gets updated at a high frequency would be a database showing traffic to a website. An example of a database that gets updated less than annually would be a Summer or Winter Games medal record table, where the event is held every four years.

Who needs to be able to access the data, who needs to be kept out?

- It's imperative for organizations to ensure the security and privacy of their data. This involves a whole host of security controls that protect a database against various compromises and threats related to confidentiality, availability, and performance.

In the next section, we'll consider what additional activities are often necessary to take data from its source and convert it into a form that's usable.

3. Preparing Data

Data often needs to be converted from its stored form to a different form that's more amenable to analysis, which we'll cover in the next section. Some have even gone so far as to estimate that the work of finding and preparing data for analysis accounts for 80% of analysts' time.[70]

What sorts of steps are involved in preparing data for analysis? Let's discuss a few of the most common steps people take when preparing data for analysis.

Finding data

In a world in which people have spent countless hours designing software to enable users to search and find digital records, this step can seem like it should be easy. But it isn't. Analysts at companies are faced with a dizzying array of data sources to search through in order to find the data they are looking for.

This struggle to get our hands on relevant data has led to two innovations: the rise of the "**data curator**" and the "**data catalog.**"

Like a curator in a museum, a person who plays the role of **data curator** on a team finds, organizes, and socializes data sources that are of high value to the organization. Such individuals may be data engineers or data analysts, but they must be intimately familiar with both the data sources as well as the needs of the analyst. They often advise data engineers on how to improve on existing data sources, they perform data preparation work themselves, and they present it and train analysts on how to make use of it.

A **data catalog** is an inventory of data sources and **metadata** – "data that provides information about other data" – along with a platform for analysts to search and find data, learn about the fitness of the data to answer their specific questions, and even interact with other analysts about the data via comments and chat functionality.

Cleaning data

Data is almost always dirty. It contains data-entry errors and typos, incomplete or blank values called **nulls**, inaccurate readings, duplicate

---

70. https://hbr.org/2017/05/whats-your-data-strategy

values, data with inconsistent units, insecure fields for which sharing would be a violation of privacy – the list goes on and on.

Part of the process of preparing data for analysis involves finding and cleaning dirty data. This can be a very time-consuming process, but data preparation software tools such as Trifacta, Open Refine, and Tableau Prep are being developed that can quickly flag issues in data sources and make it relatively easy to fix them.

But care must be taken! Dirty data that survives into the next group of activities can result in erroneous findings and therefore poor decisions.

Restructuring data

Sometimes data tables are structured in the wrong way, and need to be restructured prior to analysis. Often this mismatch in structure is caused by the visualization or analytics software the analyst wants to use that requires data in a certain format.

For example, perhaps your data source provides individual sales transactions, but you want to analyze monthly sales. In that case, you would need to aggregate the sales data by month.

Sometimes data needs to be "**pivoted**" or "**unpivoted**." For example, if you have a table with sales by product and month, that table can take one of two formats: a "tall" format with all of the sales values stacked on top of each other in a single column, or a "wide" format with sales values for each month arranged side-by-side in its own column, as shown below:

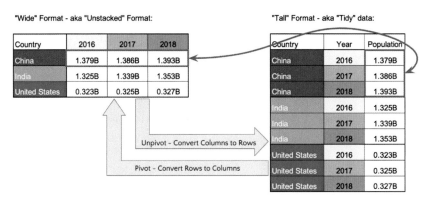

Figure 7.3. Pivoting and unpivoting data tables

Combining data

Sometimes data needed for analysis is found in different tables. In cases like these, some preparation work needs to be done to bring them together. For example, maybe the country population data for one year is stored in one table, and the figures for another year are in a different table. In this example, the data in the files would need to be combined via a **union** – the act of bringing together rows from one table and rows from another table by aligning their common column header names.

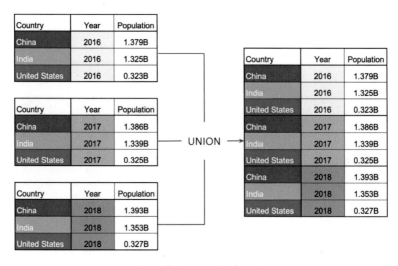

Figure 74. An example of a union

Another way of bringing data from different sources together is a join. With a join, instead of appending rows, we're bringing together columns of data. For example, maybe you'd like to compare the population of three countries in 2018 with the size of their respective economies in terms of Gross Domestic Product (GDP) for that same year. You have population figures in one table and GDP figures (measured in $USD) in another table. You can bring them together with a simple join:

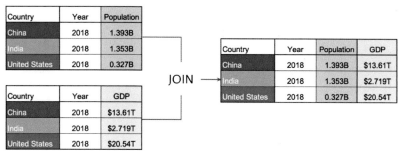

Figure 7.5. An example of a simple Join

These are very simple examples of pivots, unions, and joins using very small tables. And when larger tables are used, these operations can become much more complex, and the person doing data preparation work may have to contend with many different nuances and questions – what happens if the rows or columns don't match up, how do I handle nulls, or blank values, and so on? But you now have a basic understanding of what these activities are all about, and the good news is that it isn't rocket science.

4. Analyzing Data

Once data has been prepared for analysis, the fun part begins! The goal of data analysis is to ascend to the higher levels of the DIKW pyramid that we covered in the first chapter of the book. This involves converting raw data into information by interpreting it, and converting that information into knowledge by forming powerful associations.

The person conducting data analysis has a wide array of tools and techniques at their disposal. We reviewed five of the most common forms of data analysis in the fifth chapter of this book: descriptive, inferential, diagnostic, predictive, and prescriptive. These five approaches can be used in isolation or in combination with one another to answer initial questions, and to uncover even more important questions during the data discovery process.

There are a growing array of analytics software tools and programming languages available to the data analyst. From spreadsheets to self-service analytics platforms to data science notebooks and code, the tools at our disposal have never been more powerful. Here are just a handful of the most popular data analysis tools:

- Programming languages like R, Python and SQL (Structured Query Language)
- RStudio for R and Jupyter Notebook or JupyterLab for Julia, Python & R
- Spreadsheet software like Microsoft Excel or Google Sheets
- Data preparation software tools like Trifacta or Tableau Prep
- Self-service analytics software like Microsoft Power BI or Tableau Desktop
- Statistical software like SPSS or SAS
- Advanced modeling software like Alteryx or Knime

These tools allow the person carrying out data analysis to dive into the data, shape it, explore it, perform calculations, convert it into knowledge, and ultimately combine this knowledge with their experience and intuition to form a deeper understanding of the world around them.

For a simple example, perhaps the person carrying out the analysis would like to determine the measure of each country's economic output that takes into account the number of people that live there. They could divide the GDP by the population to estimate the "GDP per capita" – a ratio that's commonly used as a **proxy** for a country's standard of living.

Country	Year	Population	GDP	GDP per Capita
China	2018	1.393B	$13.61T	$ 9,770
India	2018	1.353B	$2.719T	$ 2,010
United States	2018	0.327B	$20.54T	$ 62,795

Figure 7.6. A table showing GDP per capita

They could go a step further in analyzing the data, and create a line chart of GDP per capita over time. In doing so, they'd learn that GDP per capita in the United States has increased steadily over the past half-century, with the exception of 2009, when it dropped by almost $1,300.

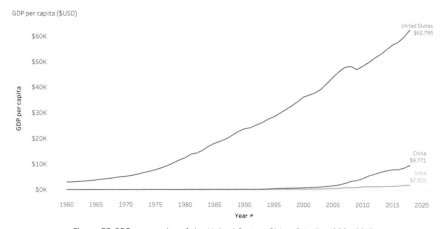

Figure 7.7. GDP per capita of the United States, China & India, 1960- 2018

If they wanted to understand what happened during that time, they could search the internet for "United States GDP decline 2008 to 2009." At the very top of the search results, they'd learn about the period between 2007 and 2009 known as the "Great Recession."[71] Note that often the best outcome of data analysis is not an answer to a question you already had, but rather a brand new question that you didn't know to ask. Furthermore, the answer to that question is rarely found in the data. You often need to consult other sources of information in order to learn more about what happened and why.

It's clear that the United States economy is much larger than either China's or India's on a per capita basis, but which one has grown the fastest? More specifically, which country's per capita GDP has grown the most relative to where it was in, say, 2000?

A simple change to the view allows the person conducting the analysis to see that China's economy has grown more than tenfold since 2000, India's has quadrupled, while the economy of the United States hasn't quite doubled over that same period of time.

---

71. If they wanted to understand what happened during that time, they could search the internet for "United States GDP decline 2008 to 2009."

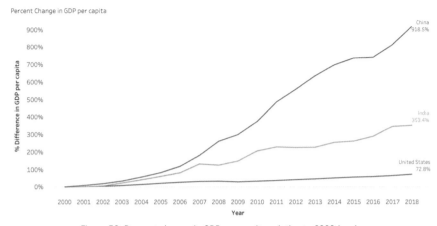

Figure 7.8. Percent change in GDP per capita relative to 2000 levels

What does a 918.5% change in China's per capita GDP mean? Well, the GDP per capita in 2000 was $959 per person and by 2018 it had increased to $9,771 per person. That's a change of $8,812. As we discussed in previous chapters, the formula for percent change is 100*(final value - original value) / (original value). In this case, that would be 100*(9,771 - 959) / (959) = (100 * 8,812) / 959 = 918.5%.

An easy way to remember what percent change means is as follows:

- If a value increased by 100%, then it doubled.
- If a value increased by 200%, then it tripled.
- If a value increased by 900%, then it increased tenfold, and so on.

The analyst could go on to ask and answer many other questions with this data and with other data brought into the mix. Is there a relationship between GDP per capita and life expectancy? Are these countries significantly greater than or less than neighboring countries in their region? Based on historical trends, by what year would we expect China's economy to double from 2018 levels? These are just a few of the myriad avenues of potential inquiry than an analyst could go down.

5. Presenting Data

Once the data has been collected, prepared and analyzed, it often needs to be shared with an audience of people. Creating and delivering notable data presentations is another kind of activity altogether and it involves very different skills compared to the other activity groups covered thus far.

Just because a person is able to discover something that they find interesting in data, that doesn't mean they can necessarily convey that insight to others in a way that draws attention and makes an impact. Fancy charts and slides often aren't enough. Statistics can be cold and boring, so the adept data presenter finds a way to bring the data to life for their audience. Bringing data to life often involves a focus on the human element – how does the data relate to real people's lives?

There's a growing focus on the role of the **data translator** in organizations. A data translator builds a bridge between data professionals and executive decision-makers. Data translators understand the language of data, they understand the needs of the business, and they act as a conduit between the two. They don't necessarily deliver presentations to large groups of people themselves. Sometimes they simply help the person delivering the presentation to grasp and craft the message. This is still presenting data, just to a much smaller audience.

There are a variety of considerations to take into account when presenting data:

The Audience: known, unknown or both?

Sometimes the person presenting data is delivering the presentation to a relatively small audience with whom they are quite familiar. For example, an executive might be presenting quarterly results to a board of directors that has a dozen or fewer members. In these cases the presenter can craft the message for that particular audience, taking into account their specific concerns, their needs, and their prior knowledge.

Other times the person presenting data is broadcasting a message to a wide and unknown audience. For example, when a journalist publishes an article containing data on a public news site, they can't be certain who will and who won't read it.

It's also possible that the presenter needs to address some people they know and others they don't know at the same time. In these cases, they must determine who is the primary target of their message, if anyone, and focus on that subset of their audience.

Here are a handful of questions to consider when crafting a message to a particular audience:

- What do the audience members care about, and what are their goals?
- Are they familiar with the data that you'll be reviewing with them?
- Are there specific terms or they are used to seeing - common industry metrics, categories, acronyms, and so on?
- Are there certain types of charts and graphs that they are used to seeing, and others that might be foreign to them?
- Are there colors, images or symbols that will convey a certain meaning to them?
- Are there specific conventions with which they are familiar - thousands separators, date formats, currencies, and so on.

Once the presenter has carefully identified their audience, the next step is understanding what they are hoping to achieve by presenting to them.

The Desired Outcome: action or mere awareness?

The presenter should consider *what they want to happen* as a result of the presentation. Do they want the audience to take a particular action or are they simply hoping to help them become aware of something? If it's the latter, sometimes it helps to think a little deeper. What should the audience members *do* with their newfound awareness?

Being able to clearly articulate the desired outcome is necessary if the presenter wants to measure the results of the presentation.

The Medium: visual, audible, written?

Another important question to consider is the medium of the message. What forms of communication will the presenter have at his or her disposal?

- Visual means like charts, graphics, or slides

- Audible means like the spoken word or music
- Written means like articles ("long-form" text) or chart annotations
- Interactive means like dashboards or applications

Each of these different medium types afford the presenter with opportunities to connect with their audience and convey information, and each of them also involve their own drawbacks and limitations.

The Delivery: live, recorded, or both?

If the presenter will be delivering their message to a live audience, they can decide how they will interact with the audience, if at all.

- What abilities do the audience members have to ask questions, provide comments, or contribute in other ways?
- Will the audience be sitting in a room together or will they be watching on their own devices in separate locations?
- Can they perform actions like completing polls or surveys or interacting with the data in some way?

These are a handful of the considerations that a person presenting data must consider in order to deliver a message that has an impact on their audience.

6. Consuming Data

Just as every one of us is involved in the first of the activity groups – creating data – so too we are each involved with the sixth – consuming data. Whether we're scrolling through our news feed, listening to our team's monthly performance review, or just having a conversation with someone about a political topic or public health matter, in each of these cases we are consuming presentations of data delivered by others.

In general we should be open to data presentations but we should also be skeptical about them and ask a lot of questions. We should always consider the source of the message, both the person presenting as well as the data itself.

- Who is the presenter and what is their **agenda**?
- What is the **source** of the data?
- What are some of the **limitations** of this data source?
- What has the presenter done to **transform** the data in any way?
- Is the data shown in sufficient **context** (relative to time, compared to population, contrasted with peers)?
- Is the data shown at the appropriate level of **detail** (not too granular, not overly aggregated)?
- How is the data displayed and what **comparisons** does it facilitate?
- What other **questions** does the data raise for you?

These are just a few of the questions we should be asking ourselves when we consume data presented by others. It's imperative for all of us that we become alert and adept data consumers. We are exposed to these forms of communication more and more every year that goes by.

7. Making Data-Informed Decisions

A subset of the people who analyze data and consume data presentations must also make a decision based on what they learn. This step represents the pinnacle of the DIKW pyramid - the application of knowledge gleaned from data. It involves more of the human element than any of the other levels below, because the decision maker needs to coalesce the two systems of thinking we explored in the second chapter – analytics and intuition – in order to know which direction to take.

Figure 7.9. Making decision based on data is application

This step is when the "rubber hits the road," changes start happening, and real people's lives are affected. It's not for the faint of heart. There are always unknowns and uncertainties about the data, and it can be difficult to predict how a decision will play out. This is part of the beauty and tragedy of the human experience. We can't expect data to be the all-knowing and perfectly objective God to save us from this tortuous path.

That's why it's better to think of making "data-informed" decisions as opposed to "data-driven" decisions. Data shouldn't drive a decision any more than fuel should drive a car. It's necessary to move forward, sure, but it isn't in control of the direction.

There are some decisions that are purely "data-driven," though. Some processes are automated and take place without any human intervention at all. An online book retailer doesn't employ a human being to manually crunch the numbers of your sales history to manually curate a list of recommended reads for you. That just wouldn't be feasible at the level of sales that some of the largest online retailers see.

But the rest of the decisions – most of the important ones – involve a "human in the loop," taking into account the data as well as the experience and intuition of a person or a group of people, weighing different alternatives, perhaps running some experiments, and finally making a call on which way to go. For these kinds of decisions, human-centered and data-informed is that way to go.

Chapter 8

THE EIGHT QUESTIONS TO ASK UPFRONT

"Ask the right questions and the answers will always reveal themselves."
– Oprah Winfrey

When we come across data in any of the three domains of life—personal, public or professional—it helps to stop and ask eight important questions about the nature of the data itself and our relationship to it.

These eight questions apply whether we encounter data as a single figure or statistic, as a table of numbers, as a visualization or dashboard, or as a complex presentation or data story. These forms, you'll recall, are the six ways of displaying data we covered in a previous chapter.

Furthermore, it's important to ask these questions regardless of the role we're in or the activity we're undertaking. All seven groups of data activities in the previous chapter apply. We need "data savvy" team members in every department and industry.

Often the answers to these questions will be quite obvious and simple. Other times one or more of the questions will be difficult to answer and complex.

No matter what their level of complexity, these questions can reveal very important truths about the data that we should be aware of. The eight questions start with the following key question words: Why, Where, Who, When, Which, What, How, and How Much.

Let's start with the first question: "Why does the data matter to you?"

1. Why does the data matter to you?

This first question is critical to establish before moving on to the next seven questions. There are many possible reasons why data might matter to you. For example, perhaps you're looking for information to help you make a decision. Or perhaps you are attempting to defend or justify a decision that you or someone else has already made. These are two very different scenarios. The second scenario is a set-up for confirmation bias: "the tendency to search for, interpret, favor, and recall information that confirms or support one's prior personal beliefs or values."[72] Watch out for that.

The context might not be decision making, but rather searching for understanding or even enlightenment. Maybe you heard someone assert a fact, belief, or opinion and you'd like to gather information that will help you corroborate or refute it. Perhaps you already know which one you'd like to do – corroborate or refute –- in which case you're in danger of falling into the confirmation bias pitfall yet again. It can be difficult to hold oneself accountable to intellectual honesty.

In either case, state your goal or objective, why the subject or outcome matters to you, and then proceed with the next question.

2. Where did the data come from?

The source of the data is of utmost importance. If someone shows you data or quotes a fact or figure to you, but they don't tell you the source of the data, you should immediately ask them to provide it. If they can't or won't, you should hold their claims as tentative at best.

There are many potential sources of data. The data could be coming from something as simple as a manually compiled list, or it could be coming from something as sophisticated as a cloud-based data warehouse.

It's also increasingly likely that the data you're considering comes from more than one place. Perhaps a database is being joined with a

72. https://en.wikipedia.org/wiki/Confirmation_bias

disparate data source such as a spreadsheet to create a custom calculation, such as revenue per state population. In this hypothetical example, revenue figures could be coming from a company database that records sales transactions, and state population figures could be coming from a spreadsheet with data that was copied and pasted from a table on the web.

Simply put, if you can't determine the source of the data, you shouldn't use it to glean knowledge about the world or to make a decision.

3. Who owns and updates the data?

Once you find out the source of the data, it's important to identify who owns it and who updates it. Who owns it could be completely different than who updates it.

For example, the database might be owned by a corporate information technology (IT) team but updated by a business team. The IT team sets up and actively manages the database, while the business team enters data into the database on an ongoing basis. For example, perhaps the business team is a group of customer service representatives who fill out forms related to questions and complaints received from customers over the phone or via online chat.

Due to the siloed nature of many organizations, it's possible that the IT team members have very little knowledge about what is contained in the database, or its relevance to the business. It's also possible that the business users know next to nothing about what happens to the data once it's entered into the system.

Furthermore, each of these owners have their own goals, objectives, agendas, and biases that can have a large impact on the usefulness and trustworthiness of the data. If call service representatives are rated based on time to complete a data entry process, they might be motivated to take shortcuts, resulting in encoding inaccuracies. If a database administrator is looking to optimize performance, they might make decisions that affect how often the data is updated.

These decisions aren't necessarily malicious or nefarious on the part of the owners. Each individual or group might simply be trying to do the best job they can do, respective to the way they are being measured.

Of course there are always cases where data owners intentionally "fudge the numbers" based on their agenda. It isn't always possible to ascertain whether the data owners are doing that, but at least identifying who they are is a start.

And while it's often best to assume positive intent, there's no need to be naive or glib. Who owns the data, what are their goals, how are they being measured, and who are they trying to please?

4. When was the data last updated?

This might seem like a small detail, but it can actually make a huge difference in what we take away from data we encounter. Time is a fundamental characteristic of the data we collect. If someone shows us a chart or graph, what is the underlying data's relationship to time?

For example, here are some more detailed questions to consider asking, where applicable:

- When were the first and last records in the data collected?
- How often does the data get refreshed or updated?
- Are all the periods (e.g. days, months, or years) full and complete, or are some only partially complete?
- If the data includes time of day, or a "timestamp," what is the time zone used to capture the time of day, and the day itself?
- Are you dealing with fresh data, or are you looking at old data that has since been updated?

Let's consider a few simple examples to illustrate the importance of this question. If we are shown data for quarterly sales that shows company revenue for Q2, the second quarter of the fiscal year, and we notice that sales have declined by 25% as compared to Q2 of last year, then it behooves us to understand whether Q2 is complete or not. If we only have sales data for two of the three months in the quarter, for example, we may well be on our way to modest revenue growth for the quarter.

If we're seeing the Q2 sales figures in a meeting after the quarter is over, then we're most likely looking at a full quarter's worth of sales. But what if we're looking at a data dashboard that has been published to a company portal or shared drive? In that scenario, there's more of a chance the quarterly figures are incomplete.

Look for a note that indicates when the data has last been updated, or ask if you don't find such a note. If the most recent update to the data happened sometime before the end of a year, quarter, month, or week, then we'll want to remember that when we go to make comparisons of different time periods. If we're not careful, we risk the pitfall of making apples-to-oranges comparisons related to time.

We also need to be aware that data values can change over time. In the COVID-19 outbreak, for example, as well as during the Ebola outbreak in West Africa in 2014, counts of confirmed cases and deaths for the disease for a given day would often change at a later date due to test results that took some time to complete. If we ask the data how many people in a certain country died of a disease on a certain day, we are likely to get a different answer on the day after than we will get a few weeks down the road.

5. Which are the most important variables?

Data sets can often be very large, and each record can be characterized by dozens, hundreds, or even thousands of attributes, or variables. Often it's impractical to consider each of them individually. So absent a data mining algorithm to sift through the attributes for us looking for patterns, we'll need to narrow our field of view to the variables that matter the most to us.

We also need to take into consideration the *form* of the variables that we deem important. Are we interested in looking at individual values, sums of individual values, statistics like averages, or perhaps percentages or rates. Sometimes a *total value* is presented to us, but a *relative value* might be of greater interest to us, or a percentage that conveys part-to-whole information.

For example, if we are interested in understanding how worldwide meat availability has changed over the course of the past six decades, we could find or create a line chart based on estimations from the Food and Agriculture Organization of the United Nations (FAOSTAT). If we found this, we'd notice that seafood availability has increased rather dramatically from around 27 million tonnes in 1961 to over 132 million tonnes in 2013:

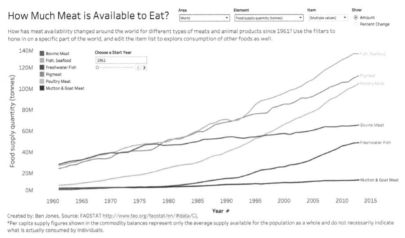

Figure 8.1. Food supply quantity for select meats, in tonnes, 1961–2013

But perhaps it would occur to us that since the population of the world more than doubled over those same years (from 3.07 billion in 1961 to 7.17 billion in 2013), it would be more interesting to consider a **per capita** availability of these types of meat (that is, the total amount divided by the population).

On top of that, it isn't typical to think of the amount of meat we eat in an entire year. It's much more common to think of the amount of food we eat on a daily basis. So if we could convert the per capita figure from a yearly amount to a daily rate (that is, by dividing by 365 days in a year), then perhaps we'd have a metric that's easier to conceptualize: food quantity in grams per capita per day (g/capita/day):

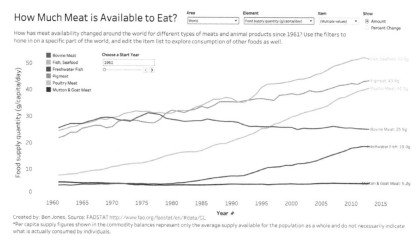

Figure 8.2. Per capita daily food supply for select meats, in g/capita/day, 1961–2013

The shapes of the curves are very similar, but now we can see that seafood increased from 24.7 to 52.0 grams per person per day from 1961 to 2013. That's a number we can relate to much more than the original 132 million tonnes figure. An apple weighs about 100 grams.

But still there's another way to look at this same data. Instead of considering the daily per capita amount, it's possible instead to compute the *percent change* in availability of different kinds of meat. The increase from 24.7 to 52.0 grams per person per day is a change of +110.7%. As we've covered in previous chapters, we determine that by using the following formula:

$$\text{Percent Change} = 100\% \times \frac{\text{New value} - \text{Original value}}{\text{Original value}}$$

Figure 8.3. The formula for Percent Change

Calculating the percent change of availability of seafood from an original value of 24.7 to a new value of 52.0, we get:

$$100\% * (52.0 - 24.7) / 24.7 = +110.7\%$$

How does the increase in worldwide seafood availability compare with the percent change in availability of other types of meat over this same time? If we compare in terms of percent change, we see that availability of poultry meat (+421.1%) and freshwater fish (+358.8%) has increased much more, as compared to how much of these types of meat was available back in 1961:

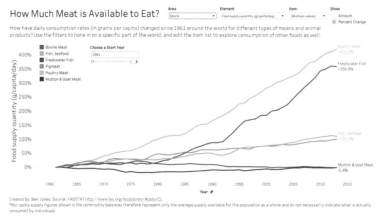

Figure 84. Percent change in worldwide per capita availability of select meat types, 1961-2013

We might also consider that evaluating food availability on a global scale isn't that meaningful for a person in a specific place of the world. And so we could fine-tune our questioning by specifying countries of interest and filtering based on those geographic criteria.

None of these ways of looking at the topic is necessarily right or wrong. Which ones we deem most important or relevant depends on how we answered the very first question on our list: "Why does the data matter to you?"

For example, if our focus is on the mistreatment of animals within the massive food factories required to provide meat at this level of abundance, we'd want to take other variables into consideration, like animal lifespan or square footage of animal production facilities. If we're trying to understand food waste, we'd need to search for consumption data and see whether it's possible to compare these values.

6. What are the definitions of the important variables?

Sometimes variables in a dataset aren't quite what we think they are. For example, in the previous example looking at worldwide meat statistics, we were careful to define the various variables we considered as food *availability* as opposed to food *consumption*. If we look carefully at the footer of the line charts, we see the following note:

> *Per capita supply figures shown in the commodity balances...represent only the **average supply available** for the population as a whole and do not necessarily indicate what is actually **consumed by individuals**.*

Without this note, a reader who casually glances at the chart might misperceive that they are looking at increases in meat consumption as opposed to meat availability. Depending on the amount of meat wasted or discarded for one reason or another, there might actually be a large difference between consumption and availability.

We can look for similar definitions of other important variables in the metadata or documentation of the database, or in the appendix or notes of the reports. If we don't see such definitions, we should ask for them.

Returning to the COVID-19 example, when we are looking at the number of cases per country, we are looking at *confirmed cases*, not *actual cases*. This is an important distinction, because there are many ways in which a person who has the disease won't end up included in the officially reported figures.

When it comes to data definitions, the devil is in the details. It may seem like a tedious process, but it helps to ask for a thorough data dictionary or metadata repository, especially if we are going to use data to make an important decision.

7. How was the data measured, collected, and stored?

Every data value is created by a process and a measurement system that can involve human inputs, machine inputs (sensor or software based), or both.

If you're looking at customer satisfaction scores, how were these scores obtained? Was the data obtained from a survey or a questionnaire?

Was it conducted in person or electronically? Was it anonymous? Who was sent the survey? Was survey completion optional or mandatory? All of these questions and many more help us determine what the survey responses actually mean.

For another example, let's say we come across a date and time variable (one that includes both the day of the year as well as the time of day). It's important to understand whether that variable was entered by a human or automatically captured by a computer, such as a time-stamp. A human-entered time variable will look very different from a machine-captured one.

Let's look at this in more detail to better understand the difference. The following plot shows the time of day that pilots voluntarily report hitting wildlife with their aircraft. The size of the circles placed at the 60 different minute positions from 0 minutes to 59 minutes are proportional to the number of reports of wildlife strikes:

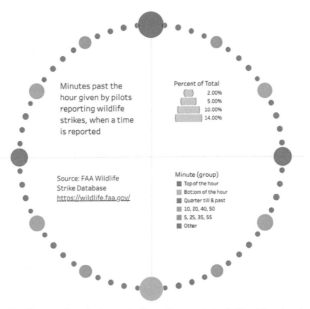

Figure 8.5. Minutes after the hour of voluntarily reported wildlife strikes by aircraft

From this chart, it's clear that pilots tend to favor multiples of 5 minutes, especially the top or bottom of the hour, or quarter till and quarter past. They are ten times more likely to report a time that ends with :15 (6.46% of all times reported) than with :16 (0.64% of all times reported), for example.

We can imagine how different this plot would look if somehow each and every one of the strikes were automatically recorded by a sensor mounted to the aircraft. We wouldn't expect to see a pattern quite this extreme in that scenario.

It's also possible that multiple different measurement processes are involved with the collection of the data in the figure above. Maybe the strikes reported to have happened 1 minute after the hour or 59 minutes after the hour have been determined by a machine-captured reading available to the pilot in a log or a display. It's always helpful to talk to the owners of the data and those who update it in order to obtain a better understanding of the various scenarios that arise.

We will see similar groupings of round values if we ask people to report their weight. We won't see such groupings if we weigh them on a scale and use the readings. People who answer that they weigh 150 lbs might actually weigh 148, 149, or 151 at any given moment.

The bottom line is that it helps for us to understand the way in which the data was collected. This understanding might end up being trivial, a mere technicality, or it might prove to be quite substantial.

The key point to understand is that there is always a gap between data and reality. Often, the size of that gap is affected by the measurement system.

8. How much time do you have to consider the data?

Some situations in business and in life afford us plenty of time to gather data, analyze the data, weigh our alternatives, and ponder our course of action. Other situations do not afford us this luxury.

For example, in a highly competitive market, a company might need to move quickly to capture the "first mover advantage" of a particular product category or feature. In those cases, it may help to consult what data they have to inform their decision, but waiting too long and suffering from "analysis paralysis" could prove incredibly costly.

When the COVID-19 pandemic started spreading and confirmed cases and deaths started increasing at an alarming rate, governments, hospitals and public health organizations found themselves in a difficult situation of needing more data but not having time (or, in some cases, resources) to collect it.

In other cases, it would be advantageous to slow down, carefully consider all of the data, gather even more of it if you can, fine-tune it, and analyze it from many different angles in order to come up with an optimal course of action.

For example, a professional sports team might be preparing to draft players who are becoming eligible for the first time. If draft day (the day on the calendar when teams will decide on who to select to join their team) is still months away, there's no need to hurry. It's highly certain when the decision will need to be made, there is plenty of time, and to fail to carefully consider the data would likely put the team at a disadvantage relative to the other teams.

If we think of potential scenarios along two axes: the amount of time to decide and the amount of data we have at our fingertips, then we can roughly divide situations into four quadrants according to the figure below:

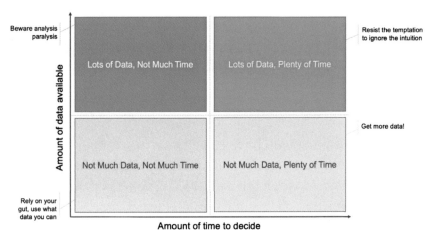

Figure 8.6. Four quadrants of scenarios relative to time and data

In the top left quadrant, we find situations in which we have plenty of data, but not much time to act. In these scenarios, we must be careful about "analysis paralysis" – the tendency to spend more time than we have looking at the data from different angles.

In the top right quadrant, we still have lots of data, but now we also have lots of time. In these situations, we might find ourselves placing too much emphasis on the data and undervaluing our instincts. As chess grandmaster Garry Kasparov said in his book *How Life Imitates Chess*[73]:

> *The things we usually think of as advantages – having more time to think and analyze, having more information at our disposal – can short-circuit what matters even more: our intuition.*

In the bottom left quadrant, we lack both data and time. In these situations, we have no choice but to move quickly. The best we can do is to use what data we have as a quick gut check, and build more data for next time, if there will be a next time, when the dust settles.

In the bottom right quadrant, we see that situations exist in which we don't have much data, but we have plenty of time on our hands. In these situations, it makes sense to get more data, and in so doing, to increase the analytical muscle we can apply to the challenge.

Both of these factors are relative, and sometimes it can be unclear just how much of each we have in any given situation. Uncertainty is a part of life, and there is certainly an intuitive component to feeling our way through these situations, and knowing how best to handle them.

Wrapping It Up

These eight questions are helpful to consider upfront when encountering data of any kind. This applies whether we're reading an article on a news site or listening to a presentation by a company executive or government official or interacting with a data dashboard or opening an email with an attached spreadsheet.

These questions don't need to take hours to answer. It's possible to run down the list in minutes or even less. If we get caught up on one of

---

73. https://www.bloomsbury.com/us/how-life-imitates-chess-9781596918276/

them, and we can't seem to find a good answer, then it's probably better that we stop right there.

Pressing forward in a state of ignorance of the basic attributes of the data might prove to be very costly indeed.

Conclusion

THE FUNDAMENTALS ARE YOURS!

"And this is the beginning of the end."

– Guy Kawasaki

We covered a lot of ground in this book, so congratulations on finishing this phase of the journey! The goals have been to demystify data, to help us see that we are already an active participant in the data revolution taking place, and that each one of us has what it takes to become more proficient in this language that is being used every day all around us.

Each of the eight main chapters covered a different topic, and the number of subtopics in each chapter increased along with the chapter number, making it easier to remember the list:

1. The ONE Overall Goal of Data
2. The TWO Systems of Thinking
3. The THREE Domains of Application
4. The FOUR Types of Data Scales
5. The FIVE Forms of Data Analysis
6. The SIX Ways of Displaying Data
7. The SEVEN Groups of Data Activities
8. The EIGHT Questions to Ask Upfront

First, in Chapter 1, we considered the ONE overall goal of data: to become wiser in our ability to apply knowledge well. The DIKW pyramid helped us see how we can move beyond mere *collection* of raw data by generating information through *interpretation*. Then we learned that we create knowledge when we join that information together with other pieces of information via *association*. Finally, we considered how to grow in wisdom through *application* of that knowledge. A key aspect of this ascension up the DIKW pyramid is that we add more and more of the human element the higher we go.

We then moved on in Chapter 2 to think about thinking itself – how our minds use TWO different processes in order to make sense of our environment and to move forward. This dual processing theory is great news for data novices. Why? Because all of our experience and intuition – what our gut is telling us in a situation – can be brought together with our newfound data sensibilities to generate even more powerful insights than we could develop with either process alone. Analytics doesn't replace intuition; it complements it. The two counterbalance each other, and can serve as a "check and balance" in the decision-making process.

In the subsequent chapter, we appreciated that data applies to more than just our careers and our employers; it's also highly relevant to our personal lives as well as our communities and society as a whole. The THREE domains of application – personal, public, and professional – expand our horizons about the usefulness of data in the world in which we live.

We then transitioned from the high level of domains of application to the very granular level of the data values themselves: how we measure the world and the FOUR types of data scales that our variables can fit into. We started by dividing data values into two main groups, categorical and quantitative. We then saw that categorical values can either be nominal or ordinal, depending on whether the category levels have an inherent order to them. Similarly, we learned that quantitative variables can be split up into two types – interval and ratio scales – depending on whether or not zero is associated with a complete absence of the variable. We used the acronym NOIR to remember these four scales, and then we considered the warning that we shouldn't apply this typology too rigidly in our analysis.

In the fifth chapter, we considered the FIVE forms of data analysis: descriptive, inferential, diagnostic, predictive, and prescriptive. We considered in what scenarios these different types of analysis can be best put to use, and we dove into examples to become more familiar with the sorts of questions they answer.

Next, we considered the SIX ways of displaying data: figures, tables, statistics, visualizations, dashboards, and data stories. These each have their respective strengths and weaknesses, and different situations call us to use different displays of combinations thereof. It can be a frustrating experience when the form of display doesn't facilitate the type of question or task we need to complete. On the other hand, it can be quite empowering when the form is matched well to the need of the moment.

We moved on to consider the SEVEN groups of data activities: creating data, building data sources, preparing data, analyzing data, presenting data, consuming data, and making data-informed decisions. On any given day, we participate in more than one of these activities. And we can augment our own capabilities with those of others by joining on teams that work together to get the job done. Even though these activities are listed in a specific order, they don't strictly proceed in a linear, stepwise fashion, but are instead always occurring, flowing back and forth in a fluid manner.

And finally, we wrapped up the Fundamentals content by considering EIGHT important questions to ask about our data upfront: why does it matter, where does it come from, who owns and updates it, when was it last updated, which are the most important variables, what are their definitions, how were they measured, and how much time do we have to make use of it? The answers to these questions will help guide us to use the data in appropriate ways, and avoid using it in inappropriate ways.

Third Party Images Used:

https://commons.wikimedia.org/wiki/File:The_Human_Element.png

https://commons.wikimedia.org/wiki/File:The_joy_of_the_happy_face_by_ Rasheedhrasheed.jpg

https://commons.wikimedia.org/wiki/File:BlindenSchachuhr.jpg

https://commons.wikimedia.org/wiki/File:Driving_a_Chariot_using_a_Snake_Whip_ (5984643299).jpg

https://en.wikipedia.org/wiki/File:Katha_Upanishad_1.1.1_to_1.1.3_verses,_ Krishna_Yajurveda.jpg

https://en.wikipedia.org/wiki/File:T_comp_61-90.pdf

https://freesvg.org/wine-bottle-and-glass-of-red-wine-vector-image

Fig 4.3: https://www.pexels.com/photo/photo-from-above-of-vehicles-parked-near-building-753876/

Fig 5. : https://commons.wikimedia.org/wiki/File:Lake_Union_Park_ (19569751209).jpg

Fig 5. : https://unsplash.com/photos/1-aA2Fadydc

Fig 5.7: https://commons.wikimedia.org/wiki/File:Dewey_Defeats_Truman_(AN-95-187)_resized.jpg

Fig 5.11: https://commons.wikimedia.org/wiki/File:Cartesian-coordinate-system.svg

Fig 6.1: https://commons.wikimedia.org/wiki/File:Human_visual_pathway.svg

Fig 6.2: https://commons.wikimedia.org/wiki/File:Tally_marks.svg

Fig 6.4: https://en.wikipedia.org/wiki/Plimpton_322#/media/File:Plimpton_322.jpg

Fig 6.5: https://www2.census.gov/library/photos/1800-a.jpg

Fig 6.6: https://en.wikipedia.org/wiki/VisiCalc#/media/File:Visicalc.png

Fig 6.7: https://en.wikipedia.org/wiki/Relation_(database)#/media/File:Relational_ database_terms.svg

Fig 6.10: https://commons.wikimedia.org/w/index.php?curid=9838454

Fig 6.11: https://en.wikipedia.org/wiki/A_Chart_of_Biography#/media/ File:PriestleyChart.gif

Fig 6.12: https://en.wikipedia.org/wiki/William_Playfair#/media/ File:Playfair_TimeSeries-2.png

Fig 6.13: https://en.wikipedia.org/wiki/Florence_Nightingale#/media/ File:Nightingale-mortality.jpg

Fig 6.15: https://www.cs.ubc.ca/~tmm/vadbook/eamonn-figs/fig5.1.pdf

Fig 6.16: https://en.wikipedia.org/wiki/Dashboard#/media/File:Dashboard_(PSF).png

Fig 6.17: https://www.pexels.com/photo/black-car-instrument-cluster-panel-945443/

Icons

Broom: https://thenounproject.com/icon/686579/

Decision sign: https://commons.wikimedia.org/wiki/ File:Toicon-icon-feather-decide.svg

38087812R00097